You

Your Body Clock

J.M. Waterhouse
Senior Lecturer, Department of Physiological Sciences,
University of Manchester

D. S. Minors
Senior Lecturer, Department of Physiological Sciences,
University of Manchester

and

M. E. Waterhouse
Department of English, Poundswick High School,
Manchester

Oxford New York Tokyo
OXFORD UNIVERSITY PRESS
1990

Oxford University Press, Walton Street, Oxford OX2 6DP

Oxford New York Toronto
Delhi Bombay Calcutta Madras Karachi
Petaling Jaya Singapore Hong Kong Tokyo
Nairobi Dar es Salaam Cape Town
Melbourne Auckland

and associated companies in
Berlin Ibadan

Oxford is a trade mark of Oxford University Press

British Library Cataloguing in Publication Data
Waterhouse, J. M.
Your body clock.
1. Man. Biological rhythms
I. Title II. Minors, D. S. III. Waterhouse, M. E.
612.022
ISBN 0–19–261982–9

Library of Congress Cataloging in Publication Data
Waterhouse, J. M. (James M.)
Your body clock/J. M. Waterhouse, D. S. Minors, M. E. Waterhouse.
p. cm.
1. Biological rhythms. 2. Chronobiology. I. Minors, D. S.
II. Waterhouse, M. E. III. Title.
QP84.6.W37   1990   612'.022—dc20   90–7673
ISBN 0–19–261982–9 (pbk.)

Typeset by Cambrian Typesetters, Frimley, Surrey
Printed in Great Britain by
The Guernsey Press Co. Ltd.
Guernsey, Channel Islands

Preface

We all have a body clock. It is responsible for waking us up in the morning and sending us to sleep at night. It affects our ability to perform mental and physical work, our body temperature and how cold we feel, and our digestive system and how healthy our appetite is. It also controls our heart and hormones and even those times when we are most likely to have an asthma attack. In fact, our body clock is responsible for adjusting us to fit into an environment dominated by the 24-hour rhythm produced by the sun shining upon our rotating Earth. The body clock can go wrong or be tampered with by our modern life-style, so that insomnia, jet-lag, and the malaise of shift-work can affect us all.

Recent scientific research has enabled us to piece together how the body clock works and is controlled in healthy people. This means that we can better understand some illnesses, offer advice to travellers across time zones and to shiftworkers, and even improve the treatment of some clinical disorders.

This book is an introductory and yet up-to-date account of this rapidly developing field of research; and, to demonstrate how the body clock influences us all, we suggest ideas for you to try out for yourself, as well as give advice that helps you to live *with, not against*, your body clock.

Manchester   J.M.W.
July 1990   D.S.M.
                                                                M.E.W.

Acknowledgements

The advent of word processors has facilitated changing a manuscript, but it has done nothing to make our handwriting and instructions easier to understand. We thank Mrs J. Stafford, who produced the first draft, and Mrs J. Clark, who dealt with all later stages, for their expertise and patience in this venture.

Also we acknowledge our debt to many colleagues and researchers in chronobiology whose ideas and data we have used freely in producing this book. We thank in particular Mr J. D. M. Coe for his constructive criticism of a draft of part of the book.

Contents

Part II · Your body clock in disorder

How to use this book

The book is divided into two main parts. In Part I we consider the basic evidence which describes the presence and make-up of our body clock and the rhythms it produces. In Part II we apply this knowledge to an understanding of:

● problems that can arise when the system goes wrong;
● difficulties that follow after we have changed our life-style such as after a time-zone transition or during shift-work;
● the usefulness of rhythms in clinical practice.

In addition we want the reader to become as involved in the field as possible and to gain some idea of how the scientific method works. Therefore, at several points in the text we invite readers to test themselves, to try to solve some problems, and to make use of their knowledge of their own body clock.

Part I

Your body clock in health

Our subject is the body clock; how it influences our physiology and behaviour and how it interacts with the rhythms in our environment.

In this part of the book we will attempt to answer the following questions:

- What experimental evidence leads us to believe that we possess an internal body clock?

- What do we know about the rhythms that the clock controls.

- Is the clock the same in all of us and at all stages of our lives?

- What do we know about the clock itself— where is it, what influences it, and how does it work?

- What is the usefulness of such a clock?

1

Body rhythms: internal and external causes

A rhythmic world

We live in a rhythmic world. From early childhood we are all aware of the annual cycle of the season and its effect on nature, from the general sense of dormancy in the winter to the burst of light, warmth, colour, and activity in summer. Every year we observe the changes in heat and length of daylight, the migrations of birds, the falling of leaves in Autumn, and the rebirth of plant and animal life in Spring. These seasonal changes arise because our planet's axis is not vertical but tilted slightly. As a result, as the Earth goes around the sun once every year, its two hemispheres alternate between receiving the sun's rays more directly (in summer) or obliquely (in winter). In addition to these annual changes, there are daily ones and it is these and the responses of living organisms to them that are the subject of this book.

The distinction between night and day is one of the most

pervasive rhythms that we experience. The Earth spins on its axis, exposing us to, and hiding us from, the light of the Sun. The time taken to complete one revolution of the Earth is decreasing over aeons of time but at the moment it is, give or take the odd second, 24 hours; this defines the solar day. Many aspects of our environment show a rhythm with a period of 24 hours as a result of this solar day. Thus the periods of lighting, heating, mixing of the water in inland lakes, and the existence of on-shore or off-shore winds all have a value of 24 hours and are caused by the daily spinning of the Earth and the apparent movement of the Sun that this produces.

But it is not only the Sun which appears to orbit the Earth. The Moon does also, and it can exert a more powerful effect where tides are concerned. The Moon and everything that is on our planet's surface mutually attract each other. Thus, two huge 'bulges' of water appear in the oceans, one facing towards the Moon and another facing away from it. These bulges are the cause of our high tides. Because the Moon revolves around the Earth, the lunar day—the time it takes for the Moon to appear at equal heights above the horizon on successive occasions—is longer than 24 hours. It is about 24 hours 50 mins. Thus with respect to solar time, the tides get later each day.

Only occupants of the deep oceans or the darkest recesses of caves will escape such rhythmic influences and live instead in a world where the passage of daily time has no obvious consequence and where tides have no effect. Even here, some annual changes might be seen such as the amount of detritus that showers down from the ocean surface or the species of animal sheltering in the cave.

Rhythmic responses in living organisms

It is not only the environment but also the animals and plants that inhabit it that display rhythms. This can be seen most clearly when considering their behaviour. Many animals are diurnal—that is they are active in the daytime and inactive at night—whereas nocturnal creatures show the opposite orientation. In addition, particularly in hotter regions, there are animals that are active about the times of dawn and dusk when it is not too hot or cold. We are all aware to some degree of the daily rhythms of nature around us. Few people have not woken to the sounds of the dawn chorus nor seen moths drawn to artificial lights as daylight fades. Birds become quieter in the afternoon, while butterflies and other insects are more active, feeding on the opened flowers. At twilight, mosquitos and midges appear and then, as darkness falls, nocturnal creatures such as hedgehogs, owls, and bats take over. Flowering plants also respond to their environment as shown by the charming example of Linneaus' flower clock (Table 1.1). Their responses affect the habits of nectar-seeking insects and the type of pollen that is being spread at a particular time of day. If the day is sunny, as drying proceeds, clouds of wind-borne seeds will be released or pods will open, often scattering their contents explosively.

Table 1.1 Linnaeus's Flower CLock

0600	Spotted Cat's Ear opens
0700	African Marigold opens
0800	Mouse Ear Hawkweed opens
0900	Prickly Sowthistle closes
1000	Common Nipple Wort closes
1100	Star of Bethlehem opens
1200	Passion Flower opens
1300	Childing Pink closes
1400	Scarlet Pimpernel closes
1500	Hawkbit closes
1600	Small Bindweed closes
1700	White Water Lily closes
1800	Evening Primrose opens

Carolus Linnaeus (1707–1780)

Humans are normally diurnal, but we are not as immutable as plants or other animals. Some of us have to work at night and sleep during the day. The developments of artificial light and packaged food have enabled us to develop a certain independence from the natural environment. Even so, reasons of convenience generally result in our synchronizing our times of sleep, leisure, and meals, and night workers often adopt a 'normal' timing for their life-style during their rest days.

Accepting that we respond to our environment, whether it is natural or artificial, we can see that these responses appear to produce further changes in us. We are just under one inch taller on getting up in the morning than we are on going to bed at night. This is because, during sleep, our spine no longer needs to support the weight of our body. Therefore, fluid passes into the discs between our vertebrae, causing them to swell slightly and this makes us taller. When we get up, the weight of our bodies compresses these discs and squeezes out the extra fluid. Normally half of this 'extra' height is lost in the first hour after waking but, if exercise is taken on waking, then the loss of height is more rapid. These results suggest that our rhythm of sleeping and being awake—in turn a response to our rhythmic environment—causes the changes in our height. Support for this idea comes from the following observations.

● If sleep is taken during the daytime, then height is gained in the same way as during a normal night.

● If you stay awake at night and do not lie down, the increase in height does not occur.

Other animals and plants also show physiological and biochemical changes that appear to result from the organisms' responses to their environment. Is this the whole story? Is a living creature rhythmic wholly because it is driven by a rhythmic environment and life-style?

Rhythms do not result only from our habit and environment

To answer this kind of question, detailed measurements of physiological or biochemical processes are required. Two examples are shown in Fig. 1.1. Body temperature is higher in the daytime than at night, and urine flow is lower overnight. Could these rhythms also reflect our environment and life-style? To some extent, this is indeed the case.

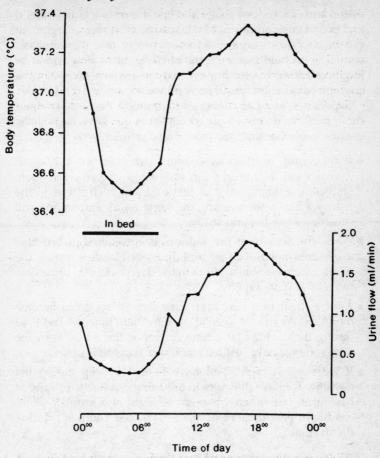

Fig. 1.1 Hourly records of body temperature and urine flow in humans living a normal life-style.

Higher body temperatures in the daytime could be the result of our greater activity when it is light, with muscle effort producing the increased heat. In addition, environmental day-time temperatures would be higher, and heat loss from our body would be more difficult, whilst heat gain from the sun would be greater. All these factors are reversed at night when we are asleep and inactive in a cooler and less interesting environment, and body temperature would fall as a result. A similar argument can be applied to urine production except that the emphasis would be on fluid intake. Thus, at night, urine flow would be low because we cannot drink when we are asleep, and in the daytime our kidneys would respond to an increased fluid intake.

Experience, however, indicates that, unlike the case of height, these rhythms do not result wholly from our life-style and the environment. Consider the following examples.

- With regard to thermal comfort (whether we think our environment is too hot or too cold), a particular room temperature might make us feel cold and even shiver in the morning but in the evening the same room temperature will sometimes feel hot and stuffy.

- When the activity of our kidneys is considered, a bed-time drink does not waken us by filling our bladders during the night, whereas a similar drink in the daytime causes urine flow to increase quite rapidly.

- After a flight to a new time zone our life-style can become muddled. We cannot sleep at the new night time, we feel tired during the daytime (at a time corresponding to night in the time zone we have just left), and our appetite is upset.

- If we work at night, and have to try to sleep during the daytime, we have difficulty in adjusting our habits in spite of having an 'active' environment at night and a quiet, sleep-conducive environment (a quiet, darkened bedroom) during the daytime.

All these examples suggest that there is something else, over and above a response of the body to our life-style and environment. A clue as to what this might be comes from our personal experience if we attempt to miss a night's sleep and stay up all night (Fig 1.2). In this circumstance we feel more tired as the evening and the night wear on. This is intuitively what we would expect and we would say that it was due to a lack of sleep. In practice, however, from about 5 o'clock in the morning onwards changes occur that cannot be explained in this way. During the latter part of the night, in spite of having had no

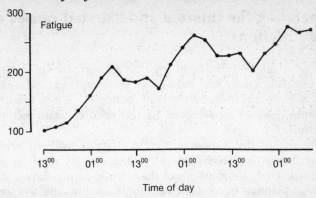

Fig. 1.2 3-hourly ratings of fatigue (arbitrary units) in a group of soldiers staying awake for 3 consecutive days.

sleep, feelings of fatigue begin to diminish. Indeed, by about the middle of the morning we feel surprisingly alert—we might even not bother with sleep after all—and we appear to have overcome the effects of a lost night's sleep. By contrast, later the next evening, we will find that our fatigue increases very markedly and we will feel much more tired than on the previous evening. That is, in addition to the tendency to feel tired because we have been awake a long time, there is some rhythmic change that decreases our fatigue at some times and increases it at others.

Observations such as these suggest that there are rhythmic changes in our bodies that are produced by some internal factor in addition to those produced by our environment and life-style. In practice we distinguish between the external cause of a rhythm, which is caused by our life-style or environment, and another internal cause, which we might say is due to a clock within our body. The rhythms we shall consider in this book all consist of a mixture of internal and external causes. (In the example of body height given above, the internal cause of the rhythm is unusually small.) We shall consider their importance to us and how they are produced by combinations of our body clock, life-style and the environment.

Separating the internal and external causes of body rhythms

Having established that body rhythms are a mixture of internal and external causes, we need to have some experimental means by which we can measure the contribution of each to the total rhythm. This can be achieved by use of a 'constant routine' experiment.

The aim of this experiment is to study individuals under circumstances in which the external causes of rhythms are removed. First, we must make the environment constant and study individuals in constant lighting, humidity, and tempera- ture. Second, we must keep the life-style constant. To achieve this, individuals remain awake and seated for a full 24 hours (the time for the rhythm to show a full cycle) and the way they spend their time is as constant as possible. Time is passed by reading, writing, listening to music, playing cards, doing jigsaws, etc. Meals also have to be modified so that they do not produce a rhythmic input to the body. One way is to arrange that an identical snack is taken every 3 hours throughout the day and night. In our experiments, subjects had to be more heroic since they had an identical 'snack' of milk, salt solution, a plain biscuit, and orange squash every hour—a way of ensuring an adequate but non-rhythmic intake of fluid and salts during the experiment.

Such 'constant routines' remove all external rhythms since both the environment and the life-style of the individuals have been constant throughout the 24 hours. What happens to the daily rhythms under such circumstances? Two examples are shown in Fig. 1.3. This figure shows that daily rhythms are less marked but show a similar pattern (that is, general shape and timing) when measured in the absence of external rhythms. The rhythm that persists in such constant routines must be caused internally and it is produced by the body clock. In addition, the differences we see between the rhythm measured normally and under constant routine conditions must be due to external causes (rhythms in our life-style and environment). Not only does this result confirm that the rhythm we measure under normal circumstances (in Fig. 1.1, for example) has an external as well as an internal cause but also it enables us to compare their size. Thus the two causes appear to be of a similar size in the case of body temperature (Fig. 1.3, top) but the internal cause in the case of urinary flow (Fig. 1.3, bottom) is rather smaller,

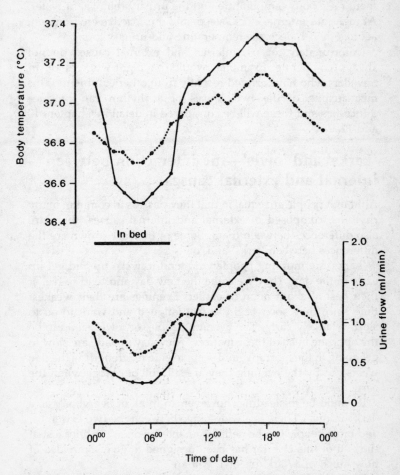

Fig. 1.3 Hourly records of body temperature and urine flow in humans living a normal life-style (full line) and on a 'constant routine' (dashed line). Time spent in bed applies to a normal life-style only.

with daytime and night-time values on the constant routine being more similar. The 'constant routine' experiment also tells us one other important fact about the two causes of our rhythms; that normally they are similarly timed. For example, during the daytime the internal clock as well as our life-style and environment raise body temperature and the urinary removal of water. At night our internal clock, sleep, and our inactive environment act together to decrease temperature and urinary loss.

Unfortunately for us, internal and external causes do not always co-operate. Examples would be night-workers or in travellers who have arrived recently from other continents. This mismatching of the two causes of a rhythm can produce difficulties and these will be considered in detail in Chapters 10 and 12.

'Larks' and 'owls'—the interaction between internal and external causes

Although people are equal in that they possess in common many rhythms, composed of external and internal causes, there are also differences between them. Some of the best known are the differences between 'larks' and 'owls'.

'Larks' are morning people who tend to wake up and get up early in the day. They welcome the new day and tend to feel at their best at about noon or earlier. Evenings are their weakest time since they soon begin to feel fatigued and want to go to sleep relatively early. The evening people, or 'owls', tend to be the opposite in all of these matters. They stay up late, are slow to get going in the morning, and seem to gain in strength as the day wears on. By the evening they are still full of energy when the early risers wilt.

It would be misleading, however, to think of everybody as a 'lark' or 'owl'. There is a wide range between the two extremes, and most people can be defined as 'intermediate'. A brief test at the end of this chapter has been designed to give some idea of how much of a 'lark' or 'owl' you are.

Why are some of us 'larks' and others 'owls'? Is it a function of our body clock or our life-style, or due to some interaction between the two?

Just as we differ in mental and physical characteristics, so too do we differ when the detailed properties of our body clock are considered. There is evidence that the body clock of 'larks' runs faster than average, so that there is a tendency for the clock to wake them up earlier—and make them feel tired earlier. The 'owls' have clocks that run slower than average so that later bedtimes and a tendency to 'lie-in' are more likely.

In addition, 'lark' and 'owl' characteristics can be created by circumstances. Thus, those whose work necessitates an early start (for example, farmers, bakers, some factory workers, and long-distance commuters) will routinely time their life-style (retiring, rising, and meal times) earlier than average and their environment—when it is dark or light, noisy or quiet—will be adjusted to match. By contrast, some sections of the community (for example, students, disc jockeys, and casino croupiers) plan their life-styles and environment to be much later than average. Often such a life-style—and, with it, the timing of daily rhythms—continues into retirement due to habit rather than need.

Whether we are a 'lark' or an 'owl' can depend upon the properties of our individual body clock as well as the timing of our life-style. Sometimes the two reinforce each other. Thus an 'owl' will often pursue his hobbies or interests late into the night so that his preferred life-style will accentuate the natural tendency of his clock. By contrast, 'larks' might tend to avoid late-night parties in favour of early morning exercise: a matching of their chosen life-style and the properties of their body clock. It might be imagined that an individual with a 'lark'-like clock but an 'owl'-like life-style or vice versa would have difficulties. This is indeed the case and will be covered when shift-work is considered in Chapter 12.

Now try this: 1.

Are you a 'lark' or an 'owl'?

For each of the following questions choose the most appropriate answer. *Do not cross-check your answers.* (The questions are based on a fuller questionnaire by Horne J. A. and Ostberg O. (1976). *Int. J. Chronobiol.* **4**, 97–110).

1. What time would you choose to get up if you were free to plan your day?

    A 0500–0600
    B 0600–0730
    C 0730–1000
    D 1000–1100
    E 1100–1200

2. You have some important business to attend to, for which you want to feel at the peak of your mental powers. When would you prefer this meeting to take place?

    A 0800–1000
    B 1100–1300
    C 1500–1700
    D 1900–2100

3. What time would you choose to go to bed if you were entirely free to plan your evening?

    A 2000–2100
    B 2100–2215
    C 2215–0030
    D 0030–0145
    E 0145–0300

4. A friend wishes to go jogging with you. She/he suggests starting at 0700–0800. How would you feel at this time?

    A On good form
    B On reasonable form
    C You would find it difficult
    D You would find it very difficult

5. You now have some physical work to do. At what time would you feel able to do it best?

    A 0800–1000
    B 1100–1300
    C 1500–1700
    D 1900–2100

6. You have to go to bed at 2300. How would you feel?

    A Not at all tired, unable to get to sleep quickly
    B A little tired, unlikely to get to sleep quickly
    C Fairly tired, likely to get to sleep quickly
    D Very tired, very likely to get to sleep quickly

7. When you have been up for half an hour on a normal working day, how do you feel?

    A Very tired
    B Fairly tired
    C Fairly refreshed
    D Very refreshed

8. At what time of the day do you feel best?

    A 0800–1000
    B 1100–1300
    C 1500–1700
    D 1900–2100

9. Another friend suggests jogging at 2200–2300. How would you now feel?

    A On good form
    B On reasonable form
    C You would find it difficult
    D You would find it very difficult

Now, score your answers. Add up the points for the 9 questions:

Q.1	A = 1	Q.2	A = 1	Q.3	A = 1
	B = 2		B = 2		B = 2
	C = 3		C = 3		C = 3
	D = 4		D = 4		D = 4
	E = 5				E = 5

Q.4	A = 1	Q.5	A = 1	Q.6	A = 4
	B = 2		B = 2		B = 3
	C = 3		C = 3		C = 2
	D = 4		D = 4		D = 1

Q.7	A = 4	Q.8	A = 1	Q.9	A = 4
	B = 3		B = 2		B = 3
	C = 2		C = 3		C = 2
	D = 1		D = 4		D = 1

Interpreting your score

Your score can range from 9 to 38. This is only a guide, of course, but your score can be interpreted as follows:

  9–15 Definitely a lark

16–20 Moderately a lark

21–26 Neither a lark nor an owl; intermediate type

27–31 Moderately an owl

32–38 Definitely an owl

Most of you will score between 21–26.

"From now on, children, you must rely on the sun, not me, to tell you the time.

2

Some properties of the body clock

Even though the role of the body clock as the internal cause of a rhythm can be investigated after removing external causes by performing a constant routine for 24 hours, this only enables us to assess the effects of the clock over a single cycle of the rhythm. In order to get a better estimate of how accurately the clock works we need to be able to study it for much longer periods of time. This suggests that we need to perform an experiment in which volunteers remain on a contant routine for as many days as possible. Not surprisingly, such experiments are rare! A Swedish study went some way towards achieving this aim by using soldier 'volunteers' and keeping them awake for about 72 hours in a constant environment. They performed a series of tests and took an identical snack every 3 hours throughout the study. The results showed that rhythms with a period of about 24 hours continued and this confirmed the activity of the body clock during the experiment (Fig 2.1). As the experiment wore on, however, there was clear evidence that loss of sleep was beginning to dominate the results, there being a progressive

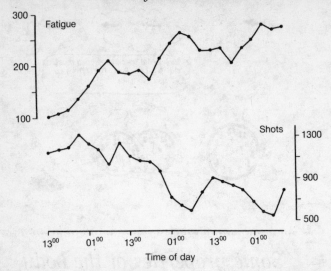

Fig. 2.1 3-hourly ratings of fatigue (arbitrary units) and speed of firing at a target (high score indicates high speed) in a group of soldiers staying awake for 3 consecutive days.

increase in fatigue and decrease in the speed of shooting at a target. We cannot be sure of how to interpret the results. Do they result from the body clock, from sleep loss—or from some mixture of these factors? In addition, investigating only three cycles of the body clock is still inadequate if we are to determine its properties in any detail—and a longer experiment is not feasible. A different type of experiment is required.

Studying the body clock for extended periods of time

Consider the following experimental design for a volunteer studied on his own. He is instructed to go to bed when he feels tired, to get up when he feels rested, and to eat meals when he estimates that it is breakfast, lunch, and dinner time. Snacks (elevenses, tea, supper) and any (indoor) exercise can also be taken when desired. The choice of food and the way to spend the waking hours are entirely at the discretion of the volunteer. The 'catch' is that, even though the time when something is done is decided by the volunteer, *he has no cues from clocks, television, or other humans as to what the time really is.* The experimenters keep a record of what the volunteer does and, by means of a hidden clock, when he does it. Because there are no constraints placed upon the timing of the volunteer's activities in such a time-free environment, these are called free-running experiments and the rhythms measured during them are known as free-running rhythms. What happens? Do individuals lose all sense of time and become erratic, or do they maintain a rhythmicity in their lifestyle and bodily functions?

Individuals do not become random in their habits. Their rhythms of body temperature and the elimination of materials in the urine, and whether they are asleep or awake and active, (the sleep/wake cycle), all continue. This is shown in Fig. 2.2 in the case of a free-running experiment lasting nearly four weeks.

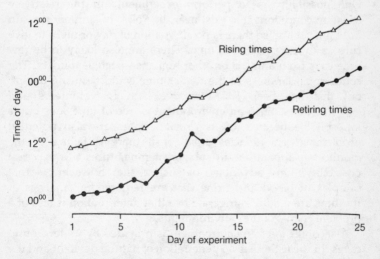

Fig. 2.2 Times of retiring and rising on successive occasions in an individual isolated from all knowledge of the passage of time, a free-running experiment.

Notice that the times of waking become a little later each day and this indicates that the cycle length is greater than 24 hours, about 25 hours in the case shown. In spite of such an unexpected result, it is important to see that the general pattern is very regular and to remember that, as far as the volunteer is concerned, he gets up at the 'normal' time each 'morning' to be ready for a full day ahead of him. (For the moment, the important point to be gained from these results is that the maintenance of rhythms, in the absence of external information about time, confirms the presence of an internal body clock. The significance of the clock running slow with a cycle length of 25 rather than 24 hours will be considered later).

Before continuing with our main theme there are a few points that may need clarifying. The first is how is a time-free environment found in order to perform these experiments?

Time-free environments

One possibility is to perform experiments in the relatively constant conditions that exist near the Poles. In summer the sun does not set and so there is no alternation of day or night to give cues as to the passage of time. There are also likely to be few time-cues from animals or other humans—such as tourists. The continuous darkness of the winter time could be made use of, but this has been less attractive both to volunteers and experimenters. Such an environment is free of time-cues but is inhospitable because of its climate. There are also potential problems if emergencies arise, or if there is failure of the monitoring apparatus—in sub-zero temperatures this is a real possibility. One advantage of such a site, however, is that samples of blood and urine that are required for analysis of rhythms are readily refrigerated so that deterioration is less of a problem than in other environments.

A second time-free environment is provided by underground caves. In these there is no penetration of natural daylight and the only sounds are those of running and dripping water. Volunteers have stayed alone in such environments for more than nine months. Clearly they are easier 'laboratories' to reach, and far less dangerous than the Poles with regard to climate and the hazards of survival. Even so, they are uncomfortable and unpleasantly damp and dark, and the need for artificial lighting and heating can produce fumes that make the situation inconvenient.

The third, and preferred, method is to build an isolation unit, specially constructed for such experiments. (We stress that 'isolation' in this context implies isolation from time-cues in the environment rather than sensory deprivation.) The first one was built in Germany and later, in 1968, the one we use was built in Manchester. Subsequently several others have appeared in different countries which differ in the sophistication of their construction and the experimental measurements that can be made.

Ours is now described in a little more detail (see Fig. 2.3). The inner chamber is designed so that up to four volunteers can be accommodated in modest comfort (though, as already mentioned, free-running experiments are performed on one volunteer only). There are areas for sleep (bunk beds), leisure (easy chairs), and eating (table and dining chairs) as well as for food preparation and washing up. Separated from the main living area are a toilet, shower, and wash basin. We have found that volunteers have no difficulty in living in such a unit, either alone or in groups of up to four. By now, over 250 volunteers (mostly university students) have taken part in our experiments, the duration of which varies from 12 to 22 days. Leisure time can be spent as an individual wishes. Often music is played, though writing letters, playing cards or chess, and even (occasionally!) revision for examinations are all activities that can be carried out. Radio and television cannot be allowed; newspapers can be delivered—but always slightly out-of-date and at random intervals so that no cues as to the passage of outside time are given.

The whole isolation chamber is housed inside an outer building and is mounted on rubber blocks so that vibration from traffic etc. does not reach the volunteers. The outer building contains a plant room which supplies and keeps constant the air supply, its humidity and temperature. The electricity supply is also regulated so that 'surges' in the National Grid—which may

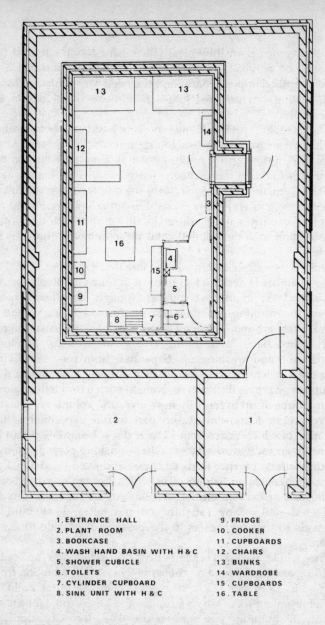

1. ENTRANCE HALL	9. FRIDGE
2. PLANT ROOM	10. COOKER
3. BOOKCASE	11. CUPBOARDS
4. WASH HAND BASIN WITH H & C	12. CHAIRS
5. SHOWER CUBICLE	13. BUNKS
6. TOILETS	14. WARDROBE
7. CYLINDER CUPBOARD	15. CUPBOARDS
8. SINK UNIT WITH H & C	16. TABLE

Fig. 2.3 Plan of our isolation unit near Manchester.

accompany the beginning or end of certain television programmes and so affect domestic lighting and identify the passage of time—are smoothed over. The outer building is also an area where recording apparatus can be housed and where the experimenters can monitor the progress of the experiment by closed-circuit television. Provided that volunteers are not allowed a watch and that they do not use television or radio then they are in an environment which combines some of the comforts of home with the more exacting requirements of free-running experiments. There is also the possibility of making many more measurements in such a laboratory than in experiments at the Poles or in caves.

It is reassuring to know that experiments performed in these three rather different time-free environments have all given results like those shown in Fig. 2.2.

Alternatives to the concept of a body clock

Another major problem that we must consider is the possibility that the continuing rhythmicity is not due to the body clock. Two alternative explanations, and our comments on them, follow.

1. The rhythm is responding to an external influence that has not been controlled in the experimental protocol.

The problem is to decide what such an influence might be. The influences upon humans of the planets, moon, and factors such as magnetic fields, atmospheric pressure, and cosmic rays have been imagined by some, including lovers, astrologers and those who, in the past, have diagnosed types of 'lunacy'. Unfortunately, when such influences are considered as explanations of the results of free-running experiments, the following problems have never been satisfactorily dealt with.

- Why do individuals have free-running rhythms that differ in length? Even though the average value is 25 hours (see p. 25), individuals show values generally within the range 24–26 hours. (As suggested in Chapter 1, 'larks' tend to be at the lower end of the range and 'owls' towards the top of it.)
- Where are the sense organs that pick up such external factors?

There is evidence for a magnetic sense in some animals, including humans. However, its role in influencing these rhythms—let alone actually being responsible for them—is not at all established. Sense organs for lunar and planetary influences, for atmospheric pressure and cosmic rays are as yet purely hypothetical.

2. The results are due to a regular structuring of an individual's life-style; they are a reflection of the regularity of our habits rather than of some body clock.

There is much to be said for such a theory. There is no doubt that individuals tend to structure their day around routines of meals, personal hygiene, leisure, work, etc. There are, however, some problems with this theory.

● It is not clear how the duration of sleep could be controlled as regularly as is observed to be the case. Even though it might be argued that a regular life-style implies a regular degree of fatigue and so will require a regular amount of sleep, in practice, such a degree of regularity is not achieved. Individuals go to bed later or earlier than average on certain occasions, as can be seen by close inspection of Fig. 2.2. For example, an individual might go to bed later than usual on one occasion because a piece of work or some leisure time activity took longer than normal. It is likely that this will make him more tired than usual and so we might guess that he will sleep longer. This would result in his rhythms running more slowly when he was interested and more quickly when he was bored (because he would go to bed earlier due to the lack of something interesting to do and so require less sleep). This idea—that longer activity spans would be followed by longer sleeps and vice versa—does not find experimental support. The reverse is seen: long 'daytimes' tend to be followed by shorter sleeps and vice versa. (Consider days 7 and 11 in Fig. 2.2, for example). This is a result that is much easier to account for if we suggest that a body clock is responsible for the alternation between sleep and activity. Such a clock will wake an individual when a certain stage of the sleep/wake cycle is reached; if he goes to bed late then that stage will be reached after a shorter period of sleep than usual. Such is the experience of most of us when we go to bed late: we might sleep slightly later than usual but rarely long enough to compensate completely for the late night. Our body clock has woken us for the next day after only a minimal opportunity for extra sleep.

● When all results from the free-running experiments are considered, the sleep/wake cycle is about 25 hours. If it were due to some 'memory' of our life-style then we would predict that about half the population would show a value less than 24 hours and the free-running periods of individuals would be distributed fairly symmetrically about an average value of 24 hours.

We have stressed the regularity that is observed in free-running experiments and interpreted it as evidence for the body clock. However, we should add that, particularly when experiments lasting several months are performed, certain irregularities do creep into the results. Occasionally sleep is missed, or is twice as long as usual. Sometimes volunteers alternate between normal and long sleeps (lasting 16 rather than 8 hours, for example) or even appear to adopt a sleep/wake cycle that lasts about 50 rather than 25 hours. In such circumstances, rhythms of food intake also can become irregular with missed or extra meals during the course of a single 'day'. However, the rhythm of body temperature generally retains its regular 25 hour period. These results do not require us to dispense with the idea of an internal body clock, if only because they appear very rarely in experiments lasting only a week or so. (By contrast, the 25-hour rhythms are regularly seen). Instead the results suggest that the system requires an occasional rhythmic input from the outside world to run smoothly. The alternatives to an internal body clock (planetary influences, cosmic rays, etc.) do not offer a ready explanation of these irregularities.

Adjusting the body clock

Even if it is accepted that there is now overwhelming evidence that we possess a body clock, it will appear to have little use. It tends to run with a period different from that of a solar day! Indeed it is this inaccuracy that leads to its often being called a circadian clock (from the latin, *circa*—about; *diem*—a day). If it is correctly timed one day, it will be approximately 1 hour late the next, about 2 hours late the day after that, and so on until it will be 'useful' again after about 3 weeks. This idea can be readily appreciated when the rising times of the volunteer in Fig 2.2. are considered. With reference to real, external time, by day 9 of the experiment he was acting like a night-worker, even though he always go up at what he called 0800 and then ate breakfast. By day 22 he was getting up at the 'correct' time (that is, his morning and real morning coincided), but had lost a whole day. Clearly this is unhelpful. Equally clearly, this is not what really happens since, if it were, rhythms would be observed to be timed irregularly when different individuals were compared. This is not so and we stress that the results in Fig. 1.1 are routinely found. The daily body rhythms are timed similarly in different individuals, and in the same individual on different days, with regular differences of only a few hours between the timing of, say, the body temperature rhythm in 'larks' and 'owls', for example.

How is this adjustment achieved?

Consider how any watch or clock is adjusted. We set it by comparing it with some reference time. This might be a radio or television programme or some natural phenomenon, for example when the sun or another star reaches its highest point in the sky. In fact the early mechanical clocks were adjusted by comparing them with sundials. (Nowadays, the use of celestial bodies for setting clocks is not widespread—a measure of how 'unnatural' our life-style has become.) The same principle is made use of by plants and animals, including man, when they adjust their body clock. The external reference that is used is the timing of one or more rhythms in the environment. The rhythm that is made use of depends upon the type of environment, the organism, and the period that the body clock will be adjusted to. Since the environmental rhythm is giving a time-cue to the organism it is called a *zeitgeber* (from the German, *Zeit*—time; *geber*—to give). Some time-cues affecting animals and plants are given in Table 2.1. Mention must be made of those creatures that inhabit the inter-tidal zone, that is the region of the shore between high- and low-tides. Their life-style is dominated by the tides rather than

Table 2.1 Some organisms and the time-cues that adjust their body clocks

Organism	Time-cue is the rhythm in:	Adjusts the period of the clock to:
Many plants and herbivores	Light and darkness	24 hours
Predatory animals	Food availability	24 hours
Creatures in the inter-tidal zone	Buffeting by waves	12.4, 24.8 hours
Newborn rodents	Mother's activity	24 hours
Some bats	Starlight	24 hours
Lizard (cold-blooded animals)	Environmental temperature	24 hours
Rat fetus	Mother's hormones	24 hours

the sun and they are adjusted to the tidal, not the solar, day. The important role of the environment in modifying behaviour, the external cause, has already been described. Clearly, there will be a wide overlap between the role of the environment in contributing to this external cause of a rhythm, its effect upon an organism's behaviour, and its ability to adjust the body clock.

Time-cues in humans

Humans are bound to be special cases, since they are more independent of the natural environment than are plants and other animals and this is an area which is not yet fully understood. Humans are synchronized to a 24-hour cycle, however, and so time-cues must exist, albeit often artificial ones. In practice, the sleep/wake cycle seems to exert an important effect upon many of our daily rhythms and the timing of many of them is determined by the time of mid-sleep or the middle of our waking hours. That is not to say that sleep or being awake are the only time-cues of importance to humans. What is likely to apply for most of us is the following scenario.

There is a whole social structure associated with our life-style. There are times when it is convenient for us to go to sleep (the shops are not open, etc.) and when it is expected that we will not be noisy. While sleeping at night we fast and are exposed to a quiet, dark environment. Waking in the morning is again normally imposed upon us by social factors—the need to get to work, to do shopping, to fulfil appointments, etc. Thus, structuring our times of sleep necessarily affects our times of food intake and activity and when we are exposed to light and an active environment. Under normal circumstances, the time-cues come as a package and is not particularly useful to separate out any one from the group; all play a role and act in harmony to adjust our daily rhythms.

Describing our time-cues in this way acknowledges that independence from the natural environment has been achieved. Unlike plants and animals we do not have to go to bed with the sun or to get up at each high tide; our man-made environment is based on a 24-hour solar day of course, but it need not be timed to coincide with sunrise or sunset. Indeed, the exact timing we choose will depend upon social and work factors and the comments made earlier about 'larks' and 'owls' will be pertinent here. For students, there is a tendency to socialize in the evenings; therefore bedtimes and rising times are fairly late. For those who must start work early in the morning (for example, bakers or farmers who have to deal with livestock), their life-style requires them to be active earlier. For those working in, or frequenting, nightclubs and casinos, their personal time-cues are particularly late. Extreme examples exist when night-workers are considered, but these produce special problems that will be dealt with later.

Individuals will also vary in the importance they attach to a particular time-cue. For example, blind people will be unable to use light/dark changes and so will have to make more use of a regular sleep/wake rhythm or of social commitments. Some people who have fewer external commitments (single, un-employed, or self-employed individuals, for example) might make less use of normal time-cues and their rhythms might even come closer to a 25-hour free-running period. When extra commitments—particular meetings, examinations, or tutorials, for example—come round then such a life-style has to be modified. To some extent the majority of us behave in this way.

At the weekends, we are no longer constrained by the timetable of our weekdays and we may have a fuller social life in the evening. Bearing in mind also that our body clock tends to run slow at the weekend, we will tend to have later nights and lie-ins, all of which cause a slight delay of our body clock. The problem begins on Sunday night when we have to go to bed early (by body time) and so we will have some difficulty in getting to sleep. The next morning we will be woken 'early' by the alarm and may experience 'Monday morning blues'. This fairly common phenomenon stresses the interaction that normally takes place between our body clock, our social commitments, and time-cues.

Whilst we stress the artificial nature of most time-cues, it would be misleading to suggest that natural light is without effect. We and our daily rhythms can respond to bright light and an appropriate use of this may become part of our armoury for speeding up adjustment of the body clock after a time-zone transition. For those living near the Poles, where such a daily cycle is missing, other artificial time-cues must be adhered to instead. Unfortunately, such people have not had their daily rhythms studied in detail and so we do not know the time-cues that are important to them.

Now try this—2.

How strong are your time-cues?

The need for time-cues to produce a body clock with a stable 24-hour period has already been described. The diary below is one way to establish how regular are the rhythms in your life-style and environment.

Fill in a log (like the example given below) every hour over the course of a 'typical week'. Mark whenever an option applies. Fill in separately the three categories of activity, lighting and food.

Scoring the log

One easy way is to calculate the percentage of possible occasions when a particular activity or environmental condition applies.

Specimen log

Day _____

Time	Activity	Lighting	Food	Drink
Midnight–0100	Sleeping	Dark	–	–
0100–0200	"	"	–	–
0200–0300	"	"	–	–
0300–0400	"	"	–	–
0400–0500	"	"	–	–
0500–0600	"	"	–	–
0600–0700	"	"	–	–
0700–0800	Standing	Artificial	Breakfast	Tea
0800–0900	Walking	Outside	–	–
0900–1000	Sitting	Artificial	–	–
1000–1100	"	"	Snack	Tea
1100–1200	"	"	–	–
1200–1300	"	"	–	–
1300–1400	Standing	Outside	Lunch	Tea
1400–1500	Sitting	Artificial	–	–
1500–1600	"	"	–	–
1600–1700	"	"	–	Coffee
1700–1800	Walking	Outside	–	–
1800–1900	Standing	Artificial	Dinner	Coffee
1900–2000	Exercise	Outside	–	–
2000–2100	Sitting	Artificial	–	–
2100–2200	"	"	–	–
2200–2300	"	"	Snack	Horlicks
2300–midnight	Lying	"	–	–

Do this for each hour of the day and do it separately for activity, lighting, meals, and drinks. Examples of this kind of analysis as applied to the types of activity are shown below (Fig. 2.4) for:

- a person on a normal routine working in the daytime;
- a night-worker;
- somebody with a very irregular life-style;
- a new-born baby;
- a watchkeeper on a merchant ship.

We will refer back to these examples later in the book.

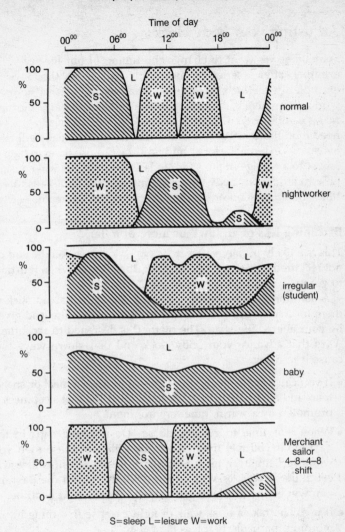

S=sleep L=leisure W=work

Fig. 2.4 Logs of sleep, work, and leisure for individuals living different life-styles. The graphs show the distribution of sleep, leisure, and work at different times of the day. For more details of how to produce such a graph, see text.

Adjusting your body clock

Sometimes we want to change the timing of our life-style. For example, after a series of late nights and lie-ins (holidays for example), it might be time to get back to our normal hours of work; alternatively, on retirement, a lifetime of early morning rising can be altered. Our body clock as well as our habits will need modification. We know that our clock is normally adjusted by various external factors—and now we can use them to help us adjust to a change in life-style. In later sections we will consider how to adjust our body clocks to much larger shifts—as after a time-zone transition or during nightwork, for example.

Becoming less of an 'owl' or more of a 'lark'

This is a likely problem after holidays or long weekends; you do not feel tired at the new bedtime but do feel tired when it is time to get up.

A solution is to make the following adjustments and stick to them for a few days while the body clock follows the lead given by your altered life-style. The method is designed to accentuate ways that advance your body clock and play down ways that cause it to delay.

- If you can't get to sleep, don't get up or have a meal or snack; relax and read quietly instead. Remember too that sleepiness is promoted by a warm, quiet environment.

- When it is time to get up, do so. Do not take naps in the daytime if you feel tired. If you do either of these then you won't feel tired the next evening . . . and the difficulties will continue. If you resist any temptation to nap in the daytime you will be more able to get to sleep at your next bedtime.

- If possible, take a brisk walk or light exercise first thing in the morning, particularly if it is light then.

- Try to arrange for your activities to be concentrated in the first part of the day and for relaxation to come later.

- Advance your meal times by the same amount as you change your times of getting up and going to bed.

Becoming more of an 'owl' or less of a 'lark'

This can occur when, for example, you no longer need to get up early for work. You wish to get up and go to bed later but you tend to wake up early and become tired too early in the evening. The advice now promotes the delaying of your body clock and guards against those factors that might advance it.

- If you wake up early, don't get out of bed but relax instead and 'snooze'. This will be easier, of course, if your bedroom is dark and quiet.

- Try to arrange for your day to start as leisurely as possible; take time over your breakfast. Similarly try to arrange for your most active work to be done later in the day.

- When you feel tired in the evening, do not go to bed yet—find something interesting to do: an evening stroll, for example or a visit to friends. It is not a good idea to sit in front of a warm fire and relax while having a quiet read as this may cause drowsiness. A nap after lunch, on the other hand, will help you to feel less tired on the evening.

- Change your meal times to fit in with your delayed times of getting up and going to bed.

Making your body clock more regular

Particularly as we become older there is a tendency for rhythms to become less regular (see Chapter 7). This need not matter but the following advice is aimed at those for whom it is an inconvenience.

- Strengthen your daily time-cues and make them as reproducible from day to day as possible. In practice this means a regularity in mealtimes, times of physical and social activity, and times of going to bed and rising. If you can make use of natural or artificial time-cues (such as daylight or traffic noise) then so much the better.

- If you wake during the night (sometimes because you need to empty your bladder) then return to bed and relax as soon as possible. Do not get up for a cup of tea or snack as this will give misleading information to your body clock.

- As you get older, you tend to need less sleep. Therefore make sure that you are not going to bed too early, particularly if you have taken a nap after lunch. People often complain of 'insomnia' in such circumstances!

3

Your body clock, fatigue and sleep

Fatigue and body temperature

We have already outlined the evidence (Chapter 1 and 2) that the rhythms of fatigue and body temperature have both external and internal causes. For alertness (or fatigue) the evidence must be based upon subjective measurements, but, for body temperature, objective measurements are possible. It will have been noted that the rhythms of body temperature and alertness are timed very similarly with higher values in the daytime and lower values at night (compare Figs 1.2 and 1.3).

This means that a higher body temperature is associated with a higher degree of alertness or a smaller amount of fatigue. The detailed explanation of what makes us feel alert is not known, but it is certain to be some function of brain activity, and brain activity increases with body temperature. This is because enzymes (proteins that are responsible for carrying out the chemical processes within the body) act more quickly as the

temperature is raised. This relationship between body temperature and the speed of biological processes applies throughout
the animal kingdom. It is why butterflies warm up before flight,
either by exposing their wings to the sun's heat or by generating
heat internally by vibrating them; it is why lizards bask in the
morning sun; and it is the explanation for the saying: 'fast runs
the ant as the mercury rises'.

If a raised body temperature promotes alertness and staves
off feelings of fatigue, high body temperatures are obviously
disadvantageous when we wish to get to sleep. We all have
experienced inability to sleep when we cannot settle down and
problems occupy our minds. Many factors can cause this but one
of them would be a body temperature that is not falling fast
enough in the evening. It is a common finding when we are jet-
lagged or trying to sleep in the day after night-work. In both of
these cases our body clock is wrongly timed for our life-style and
so it does not cool us down and make us feel more fatigued in
the hours just before bedtime.

Fatigue, body temperature, and sleep

If a link exists between body temperature and the sensation of
fatigue, then it is reasonable to enquire if the abilities to fall
asleep and remain asleep are also related to body temperature.
Experiments have been performed to investigate, at different
times of the day and night, how easy it is to fall asleep, how likey
it is to wake up spontaneously, and how long volunteers can
stay asleep. The results show that when body temperature is low
or falling then not only is fatigue higher but also sleep is easier to
initiate. By contrast, waking is more likely to occur if the body
temperature rising or has reached a high level. So, in the evening
when the body temperature is beginning to fall, there is a natural
tendency to fall asleep and in the morning, when body
temperature begins to rise rapidly, we are most likely to wake
up. Related to these results is the question of how long we can
stay asleep (in a laboratory that is always equally quiet, dark,
and warm) at different times of the day. Figure 3.1 shows that if
we go to bed at the 'normal' time we sleep about eight hours, a

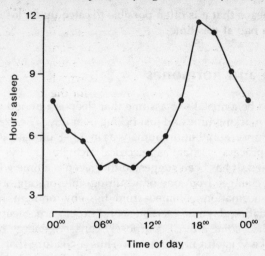

Fig. 3.1 The relationship between time of going to sleep and number of hours spent asleep. This experiment was performed in the constant conditions of a sleep laboratory.

result that most of us would accept as part of our daily experience. However, the figure also shows that if we fall asleep when the body temperature is about to begin to fall (about 6 o'clock in the evening), there is the possibility of sleeping for about 12 hours. By contrast, even if we manage to get to sleep at about 10 o'clock in the morning the sleep is likely to be shorter and broken. In effect we have considered this already (Chapter 2) when we described how delayed retiring times did not tend to be associated with longer sleeps; it was a rising body temperature that curtailed sleep and over-rode any need for more sleep that might have existed.

There is one exception to this general parallelism between temperature, fatigue, and the ability to sleep. After lunch (at about two o'clock) many of us feel tired and may take a short nap, even though body temperature does not normally fall much at this time. The phenomenon is called the 'post-lunch dip'—a reference to the dip in mental performance that occurs then. Its cause is uncertain—it is also found even if we do not eat then—

but it means that it is often possible to catch up on lost sleep by taking a nap at this time.

Sleep and hormones

It would be a mistake to assume that sleep is a period when the body is marking time and just ticking over idly. The exact role of sleep is uncertain, but, in humans as in other animals, it is a very active process as far as electrical activity in the brain is concerned. It has been suggested that sleep is a time when brain activity changes from one of acquiring, interpreting, and acting upon information obtained from the environment to one of consolidating daytime memories and experience. Sleep is also a time when some animals purposely conserve energy because it would be wasteful not to do so. Thus a creature that hunts by daylight would waste its energy if it rushed around in the night when its prey was hiding in a burrow and, anyway, it would be poorly equipped for hunting then. A third role of sleep is that it provides an opportunity for the growth and repair of tissues. This is controlled by several hormones, particularly growth hormone (in both sexes) and testosterone (mainly in men). The release of growth hormone (Fig 3.2) is dominated by external factors rather than the body clock and is linked to the electrical changes in the brain associated with 'deep' sleep. This is normally found in the first part of sleep (see below). It is interesting to note that severe physical exercise in the daytime is sometimes associated with increased deep sleep the following night; perhaps there is a link here between deep sleep, an increase in growth hormone release, and the growth of muscular tissue that is produced by exercise.

Other hormones rise at night also (Fig 3.2). These include cortisol (which rises later in the night as the body prepares for waking and is strongly influenced by the body clock); antidiuretic hormone (which is one of the ways in which fluid formation by the kidney is reduced at night, see Chapter 6); and the male sex hormone, testosterone, as well as some of the hormones that control the reproductive cycle in women. The effect of such 'nocturnal surges' in sex hormones, as the increased release of

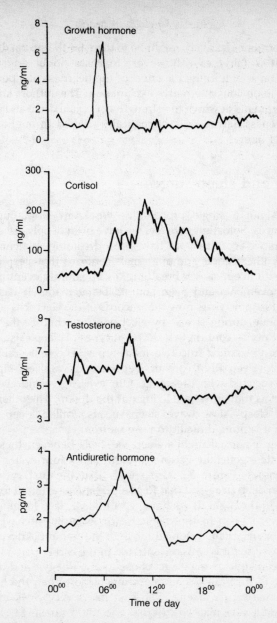

Fig. 3.2 The daily rhythms of several hormones measured in individuals living a normal life-style.

these hormones is called, might be to increase the sexual drive at night. It is fairly easy however, to caste doubt on such a suggestion scientifically; the effect of the nearness of a potential mate is an obvious alternative explanation. The authors know of no experiments in which the strengths of sexual drive and sexual receptiveness have been systematically studied throughout the whole 24 hours.

Sleep and sleep stages

Sleep is not a single process, as we know from our own experiences. Sometimes we feel we have been deeply asleep and at others we recall that we have been dreaming. Watching the sleep of other people and of animals confirms that sleep can be quiet, with deep, slower breathing, or apparently eventful with body movements and even sounds being made. It has been known for some years now that records of the electricity activity of the brain during sleep—by electrodes attached to the scalp, face and neck—confirm that different types of sleep exist. These have been classified into two main types. The first—rapid eye movement sleep (REM), dream sleep, paradoxical sleep—appears to be associated with dreaming. Our eyes, legs, and even our voice act as though we are living out the dream. The other main type of sleep—slow wave sleep—is also called 'deep sleep' because it is more difficult to raise us from.

During a normal night's sleep we cycle between these two main states, generally getting through about four cycles as the night passes. Figure 3.3 also shows that the first cycles are richest in deep sleep and that REM sleep is concentrated towards the end of the night. If we have recently lost sleep (after a week of trying to sleep in the daytime, for example) or have been awake for an unusually long time, then the amount of deep sleep is increased but it is still concentrated in the earlier part of sleep. Deep sleep appears to be a response to our life-style and reflects the amount of prior wakefulness much more than the time of day when sleep is taken. That is, it has a very weak internal cause and a very marked external one. By contrast, REM sleep shows a strong internal cause and is often used as a marker of

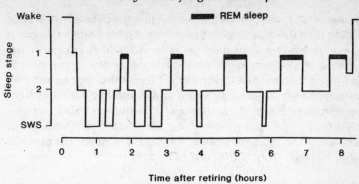

Fig. 3.3 The cycling between different sleep stages during the course of a typical night. SWS, slow wave sleep.

the body clock. Experiments in which sleep was taken at different times have shown that REM sleep is very little affected by external factors, with most REM activity in the hours between 8 o'clock and noon, and least in the hours just before midnight. It is for this reason that the amount of REM activity increases during the course of a normal night's sleep (Fig. 3.3).

If sleep is taken at an unusual time, the changes associated with it (the release of some hormones, the type of sleep) will be affected to different extents depending on whether they are dominated by external factors or the body clock. Phenomena that are influenced mainly by the body clock will be affected

Table 3.1 A comparison of sleep at night and during the day upon some hormones and types of sleep

	Sleep at night	Daytime sleep
Growth hormone	Mainly first part	Mainly first part
Cortisol	Rises throughout sleep	Falls throughout sleep
Deep sleep	Mainly first part	Mainly first part*
REM sleep	Mainly towards end	Mainly at the beginning

* REM sleep can 'squeeze' deep sleep out of the first part of sleep towards the middle of it.

more (you are sleeping at the 'wrong time' as determined by this clock) than those determined mainly by external factors. Some of these points are illustrated in Table 3.1 which compares the effects of sleep at night and during the day upon growth hormone release and deep sleep (dominated by an external cause, the act of going to sleep) and cortisol release and REM sleep (dominated by the body clock). Whether such abnormalities lead to sleep being less 'refreshing', or to other problems, is not known. At the present time, as we have described, the problem with daytime sleep is believed to be only that it is too short.

4

Your body clock, waking and physical activity

We have already considered how the body clock, by lowering body temperature and increasing the sensation of fatigue, helps to promote and maintain sleep. The opposite effect—that a rising body temperature promotes waking and alertness—is equally important, of course; but being awake and active involves other factors.

Cortisol and adrenalin

At times of stress, the body responds in a complex way; two hormones are central to this response, cortisol and adrenalin. The exact role of cortisol is unknown, but its importance can be deduced from the observation that animals that cannot produce cortisol, due to injury for instance, are very vulnerable in emergencies. Normally (see Fig. 3.2) cortisol is secreted mainly around the time of waking and this seems to be part of dealing with the 'stress' of waking up and preparing for the new day.

Excessive stress can damage the heart and it might not be a coincidence that cardiac disorders are most frequent at the time of waking or the hours just after.

Some results from the study upon army volunteers who stayed awake for 72 hours in constant conditions and ate regular meals were considered earlier (Chapter 2, Fig. 2.1). In addition to doing 'target practice' and recording how tired they felt, the volunteers collected urine samples which could be used to estimate the concentration of adrenalin in blood. Fatigue ratings, the speed of shooting at a target, and the rate of urinary excretion of adrenalin are shown in Fig. 4.1. Note that the

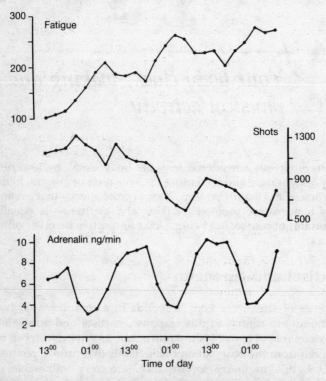

Fig. 4.1 3-hourly ratings of fatigue (arbitrary units), speed of firing at a target (high score indicates high speed), and urinary excretion of adrenalin in a group of soldiers staying awake for 3 consecutive days.

rhythm of adrenalin is timed opposite to that of fatigue and the same as that of shooting speed.

Adrenalin is another 'stress' hormone. It is released when we are angry or anxious and its release is a major part of the 'fight and flight' reaction in animals. It exerts many effects upon the body. It makes the heart pump blood faster (we have all felt the pounding and racing of our hearts when we are roused); dilates the airways of our lungs (so we can breathe faster); and causes a great increase in the release of energy—by breaking down glycogen (the form in which glucose is stored) for muscles, and fat (from fat storage depots) for the rest of the body. In sum, it enables the body to be most able to deal with danger and to be most efficient physically. The obvious fact that stressful circumstances, such as anger or danger, are not conducive to going to sleep is due to adrenalin to a large extent.

Under normal circumstances when there is no undue stress— as in the examples of the soldiers or people living normal lives— adrenalin is released in far smaller amounts. Even so, it is still an important hormone and 'tones up' the body so that it can perform more efficiently during the daytime. Equally important is its decrease in concentration in the evening, which relaxes the body so that sleep is more easy to achieve. The adrenalin rhythm is like that of body temperature, therefore, in its general timing and its general integration with the sleep/wake cycle.

Exercise and its physical demands

Can the body perform physical work equally well at all times of the 24 hours? Consider the biochemical and physiological changes that are required to exercise efficiently.

- The basic biochemical process is one by which glycogen in the muscle (a store of glucose) is broken down to release energy which can then be used to drive the muscles.

- An increased blood supply brings the extra oxygen needed for glucose breakdown and removes the waste materials (mainly carbon dioxide and lactic acid).

- An increased pumping of the heart ensures that the exercising muscles receive all the extra blood and yet enough still goes to the brain and other vital organs.

- An increased rate and depth of breathing ensures that more oxygen is taken into the blood (for delivery to the muscles) and that the extra carbon dioxide is removed from the body.

- An effective means of increasing heat loss from the body is required. This will prevent a build-up of the huge amount of heat that is produced in exercise. It is achieved by increased blood flow to the skin and an increased sweating rate.

Do daily rhythms exert any effect upon these processes? Their role during the daytime, when the body is primed, will be to increase the ease and efficiency with which such mechanisms come into play. Laboratory tests have shown that the rates of oxygen uptake and amounts of muscle effort that volunteers could develop tend to be greater in the daytime than at the night. But the position is more complex than that. Individuals were also asked to assess the severity of a task at different times during the 24 hours. Even though the task—one that involved pedalling on a stationary bicycle—was equally demanding at all times, it was felt by the volunteers to be most difficult to achieve in the middle of the night. In summary, exercise is most efficient in the late afternoon. At that time we can respond by the greatest amount and at the greatest speed and we perceive it as being least difficult.

These differences in athletic performance might not be very large, a matter of only a few per cent, but for world-class athletes, the difference between a world record and a mediocre performance can be only fractional. It is not surprising, therefore, that world records are generally broken in the afternoon, not during the night. It will also raise a few problems for sportsmen and sportswomen who are training or competing in a new time zone to which they have not yet adjusted. Thus a normal training time in the new time zone might coincide with night on home time and so lead to a physically poorer and psychologically dispiriting performance.

For the rest of us, who rarely perform at our physical maximum, these problems would seem far removed. Yet, for some, physical work at night seems more demanding than during the daytime and this is clearly another disadvantage for the night-worker.

Now try this—3

Making use of our rhythms

So far we have not considered how to use a knowledge of body rhythms to our advantage. As later chapters will show, advice can be given to travellers and shift-workers who have recently changed their routines. However, people living normal routines also can benefit from a knowledge of what their body clocks are telling them. Here are some ideas.

A comfortable room temperature

How comfortable we feel is determined not only by the temperature of the body (in effect, the temperature of the blood going through the brain) but also by that of the skin. In order to feel comfortable we must get the balance right. For example, if we have raised our body temperature by exercise or effort then cooling ourselves by taking a cold shower, a swim, or a cold drink makes us more comfortable. Also, if we are cold, warming our hands in front of the fire is very comforting. A similar line of reasoning—warm the skin if the body is cold—explains the idea of 'one for the road' or the 'stirrup cup'. The nip of alcohol causes the blood vessels to dilate and so warm the skin and make us comfortable in spite of being out in the cold. It can, however, be dangerous insofar as it promotes heat loss: your body is tending to become cold in a cold environment. As a final example consider the passage of air across the skin of our face—a very sensitive area. If our body is becoming too warm—through sunbathing, for example—then the air is a 'pleasant breeze'; if it is tending to be rather cool—seated in wintertime—then the air is a 'draught'.

Bearing this in mind, we can now look at daily changes in body temperature. In the evening, body temperature is being reduced and so tends to be slightly higher than required. You can help this fall in body temperature by being inactive all evening (sitting in front of the television?), but if you are quite active physically then you can maintain a sense of comfort if you turn down your room thermostat a few degrees in the evening or if you roll up your sleeves and aid heat loss this way. If you are active in the evening and yet do neither of these things, then you may find the room 'stuffy'. In the morning, body temperature is being raised and so it tends to be slightly lower than required. This requires a warmer environment for us to feel comfortable. Cheaper alternatives to turning up the central heating are to do a brief bout of gentle exercise, which increases body heat from the inside, or to wrap up well, which reduces loss to the outside.

Exercise and physical exertion

The usefulness of gentle exercise in the morning to help warm us up has just been mentioned. It will also help to alert us and loosen up the joints in the spine by squeezing out fluid from the discs between the vertebrae (see Chapter 1). But remember that the increased size of the discs in the morning might increase the risk of a 'slipped disc'; be careful and, particularly when lifting heavy loads, make sure that you are doing so correctly—or even delay the task till afternoon. For severe exercise, the best part of the day is late afternoon, because the body is most efficient then and you will be able to push yourself harder.

Waking up and getting to sleep

A short bout of exercise has a further role, namely of waking you up in the morning as it turns on the alerting mechanisms of the body. Other means of waking you up include hot or cold showers—tactics that 'shock' the body—or cups of coffee, containing the stimulant caffeine. In all cases, the effect of the body clock is being accentuated by our life-style, generally by means of the hormone adrenalin.

In the evening the aim is to relax the body. Therefore hot and cold showers, arguments, and exercise are not good preludes to helping you get to sleep. Also, a large meal, particularly with coffee or tea, might keep you awake whilst it is being digested (though some people find that it is easy to fall asleep after a meal). Many people practice relaxation techniques, take a long soak in a bath of warm (not hot or cold) water, or have a quiet read in bed before turning out the light. All these methods are calming us down and decreasing adrenalin release, and so accentuate the likelihood of falling asleep that is being promoted by our body clock.

5

Your body clock and mental activity

We have already established that physical work seems harder at night than during the daytime; does the same apply to mental performance? We are concerned if we perform badly or dangerously at some times and the effects of poor performance will also be of interest to managers and the general public. Managers will wish to know if the body clock means that there are times when the output of their work-force is below standard and the general public will be concerned about the possibility that safety in industrial processes, public services, transportation, etc. will be adversely affected at some times.

Some problems of measuring performance at work

Unfortunately, as soon as an attempt is made to measure 'performance', a whole series of problems arises. It can be very difficult to decide how to measure performance at many jobs. For example, how would you measure if a plumber, a lorry driver, a teacher, or a magistrate had just performed a task well? In the cases of the plumber and magistrate, is it the number of jobs or cases completely successfully?—but some are more difficult than others. For the teacher, is it how well the class has understood?—but the topic might be difficult or the pupils not very bright. How do you judge the lorry driver? By whether or not he is late? By how few times he has lost his way? Surely this depends upon the traffic conditions and the difficulty of the route.

Sometimes the position is considered from a slightly different viewpoint and only poor performance—*as assessed by accidents or errors*—is considered. Even that can be complicated. How would you establish at all reliably if a magistrate, politician, inspector, or teacher had made an error? And even if errors could be assessed satisfactorily, there need not be any clear link between full-blown errors or accidents and a performance that is generally sub-standard—as any self-critical driver knows.

In addition it is difficult to attribute more errors or a poorer performance wholly to the effects of a body clock. Consider the problems of traffic accidents more closely. If it were found that more accidents occurred in the winter months between 6 and 8 o'clock in the evening compared with noon and 2 o'clock, is this because, during the early evening, lighting is worse, there is more traffic, drivers have been working longer and are more tired, or weather conditions are worse?

It might be considered that performance at many factory jobs would be easier to assess since a product is involved. However, if one shift performs better (and 'better' might refer to the quality or quantity—or both—of product that is made) is it because it consists of more conscientious workers; their conditions of working are better, or they have less distraction; they are supervised more closely and the conveyor belt moves faster; or their body clock enables them to work better at some times of the day than others?

Clearly, if we want to know the role that the body clock plays in our mental performance, all these other influences must be controlled or eliminated.

Some improvements—but further problems

Let us consider how some of these difficulties could be removed or controlled. In principle, we require the following conditions to be observed.

1. The same workers are investigated at different times of the day.

2. The workers have been on duty for the same amount of time whenever measurements are made. (It is known that performance deteriorates after several hours of work.)

3. External factors (lighting, heating, noise, traffic conditions, weather factors) are kept constant.

4. The work being investigated is always of the same type and difficulty.

5. The individual, not a supervisor or the speed of a conveyor belt, decides the rate at which the task is carried out; this is termed a 'self-paced task'

Condition (1) can be fulfilled by requiring the same work-force to work all shifts in a rotating shift system. With sufficient manipulation of the rota, it would be possible to arrange for the work-force to have been working for the same number of hours at different times of the day—condition (2). The conditions described in (3) are sometimes fairly easy to control (for example, the amount of noise and environmental temperature), but there are other conditions (traffic density or natural lighting, for example) where this can be more difficult or impossible. In many jobs, condition (4) can be fulfilled as it is possible for similar types of work to be tackled throughout the 24 hours. In other cases this is not so. Teaching at night is unlikely to prove popular (with teacher or pupil!) and the night shift in a hospital ward cannot be made equivalent to the day shift (except for intensive care units which are continuously busy). Finally, condition (5) cannot be fulfilled in all occupations. For ambulance men and air-traffic controllers, those in 'supply-and-demand' situations, the demand is due to external factors and the workers have to respond; their work load is not self-paced.

Errors measured in the workplace

It must be apparent by now that satisfactory studies are likely to be rare. Some studies, however, do exist and a selection is shown in Fig. 5.1. We need not discuss the results in detail except to note the following points.

- Errors tend to be more frequent at night than during the day.
- A post-lunch increase in error exists.

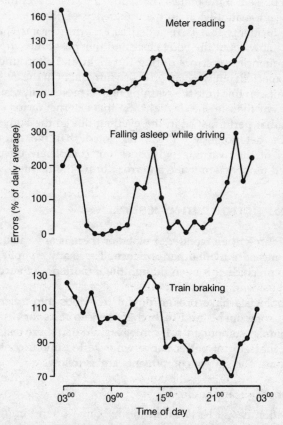

Fig. 5.1 Relationship between time of day and frequency of errors at three tasks measured on site.

Not only are the results of such 'on site' studies of immense value for what we assume they tell us about the role of our body clock in affecting mental performance, but they also serve two further roles. First, they act as a standard against which the results of other tests (below) can be measured. Second, they confirm the difficulties of interpretation that can arise, as can be seen by considering the result which shows the frequency of errors made by locomotive drivers. 'Error' here refers to the failure to respond to a warning light that comes on when a signal at red is passed. If the brake is not applied by the driver then it is applied automatically; it is the frequency of these automatic braking incidents that is recorded as an error. From what we already know about the body clock and the 'post-lunch dip', the high frequencies of errors during the night and after lunch are not unexpected; but why are errors so infrequent in the evening? It is because at this time the warning light is more easily visible in the twilight than in the daylight. So this external factor offsets the fact that performance in the evening due to the body clock might be deteriorating. It will be noted that the improved visibility of this warning light does not completely offset the increased tendency to make an error during the night.

Mental performance tests

By now it might be wondered whether there is any satisfactory way to measure mental performance. The many complications seem to preclude this even though the importance of success is as great as ever.

Psychologists have broken down 'real' jobs into a series of 'simple' components and have then devised tests for assessing these simpler components. It can be argued that these tests are a reliable indicator of performance when tested under controlled conditions. The simple components are as follows.

The sensory component

Information has to be taken in to the brain—often through the eyes but this is only because humans rely so much upon this sense. Touch, hearing, taste, and smell can all be used instead or in addition (consider how a chef, carpenter, piano-tuner, tea-taster, or perfumier work, for instance).

The central component

This is the processing of information by the brain itself. It will include reasoning or thinking and might make considerable use of long-term memory or experience.

The motor component

This is a type of action. It might be as straightforward as writing down or calling out an answer, pressing a button, etc. or it may be a task that requires manipulative skills such as wiring an electrical component or threading a needle. It might include a complex co-ordination between arms and legs as in driving a car.

Short-term memory and vigilance

There are two other components that tasks can possess, short-term memory and vigilance. These also involve processing within the brain but are slightly different from what is normally meant by thinking or drawing on memory and experience.

Short-term memory is the phenomenon by which we can remember a telephone number long enough after looking it up to be able to dial it. It enables us to remember the cards that have been played in a hand of bridge, the objects on a tray in the game of Pelmanism, or reading a meter and recording the result (see Fig. 5.1). Short-term memory is a temporary store of information and often it is irrelevant to convert the information into a long-term memory, the type of memory that enables us to recall events years later. Thus, although it might be useful to remember a particular telephone number (and so convert a short-term into a long-term memory), this is often not the case and we are unlikely to want to remember every hand of cards. That is, short-term memories are often required to be forgotten. A few people do seem to be able to remember everything (they have 'photographic memories') but this can often lead to remembering a mass of unwanted material and so things have to be actively 'unremembered'.

The other component of tasks is vigilance. Through vigilance we detect changes in our environment such as in traffic conditions, a new 'blip' on the radar screen, or a faulty product on a conveyor belt. It is a characteristic of a task requiring vigilance that it can span a long time, minutes or hours or even a whole work-shift.

A selection of simple tests

To illustrate the ways in which different components of performance can be assessed, we will consider examples from a small selection of the tests that have been devised. At the end of the chapter (Now Try This—4), we will suggest that you adapt the tests so that you can measure your own performance.

Group 1: Tests which require large amounts of sensory input

These tasks require a simple response and not much thought, coupled with the need to sift through large amounts of data in order to find a 'target' amongst unwanted information (Fig. 5.2).

```
AGBHJTYOWLNMPASDDQGTUITLMDJEX
RYHSKMXHWYUSGHWWMLQWMSPLEUJDM
UJKSEHMSKQXGKLLQTHOMPDHJJEKLO
YWTFGHIKMCCOWLXPMTXWKIRLMHJDB
POEKJDNMFKURHHNRJKSSLPLQXYJDD
QWBDHJKPLMCBSXAZIDZKLEGHLCVVE
PDMSMBBOJWSQMNXLUDTTKWKLFMRQL
BNKLFMNSGBEOPAGVSBHKFMNXBVSJH
ILDKJMSVSKIRGQNBXTYUOLLKHWTPS
WJKMVLHMLKJOLKSQMXRTKJDMPGNPP
UKDGHHXBNLQJMDELOPSGRTLNAQIFF
UJKDMFEOIPSKLFHLDDWNDSLOUFCSL
LPEJKDNFKLRUHFLLSMJCGBQKTDLRI
LKDHGRYUIEPKDSIWLGORRMFILEKMD
```

Fig. 5.2 Sample for Groups 1A or 1B (for more details, see p. 57).

A. *Cross out the E's in the following passage.*

B. *Cross out duplicate letters that are adjacent to each other.*

The letters can be chosen so that unwanted ones differ from the target by larger or smaller amounts. Thus Es are difficult to distinguish from Fs in contrast with Os and Xs, for example. How long it takes to complete the whole block of letters is measured.

Group 2: Tests which stress the motor output

Clearly some sensory input is necessary, but this and the amount of thought required are rather small in comparison with the motor response required. Often this is some form of manipulative skill.

A. *Put a dot into the centre of each circle (Fig. 5.3).*
A test would consist of about 20 'lines', each of about 20 linked circles.

B. *Threading beads onto a string.*
How many beads could be threaded in 2 minutes would be measured.

In the first case the task is easier if the targets are larger, are closer to each other and more regularly arranged. In the second case the sizes of the beads and the holes through them can vary.

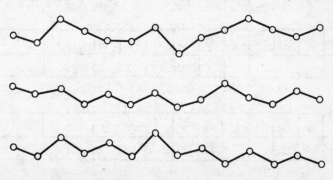

Fig. 5.3 Sample for Group 2A (for more details, see text).

Group 3: Tests stressing a co-ordination between sensory and motor components

We give two examples of these.

A. Copy each symbol accurately (Fig. 5.4).

It will be noted that a great variety of difficulty could be introduced here—both in the shape of the symbol and the standard of accuracy that is required in the answer. Typically a test might consist of measuring how many symbols could be copied in 2 minutes.

B. Substitute one symbol for another.

Letters A–F could be paired with the symbols in Fig. 5.4 and then a string of random letters, say BCEFADDB etc, would be required to be coded by use of the relevant symbol. As with test (A), the difficulty can vary greatly in both the accuracy required in the copied symbol and the similarities between the different symbols. Again, the number of substitutions accomplished in 2 minutes would be measured.

Group 4: Tests stressing short-term memory

The general format of the test is the same as that for tests (A) and (B) in Group 1. The difference is that each line has to be searched to establish the presence or absence of a target set of letters (the order of the target set is not important—only whether or not the whole set is present). Obviously, whilst scanning the letters this

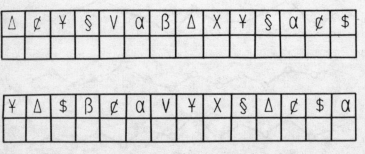

Fig. 5.4 Sample for Group 3A (for more details, see text).

set has to be remembered and it is changed for each test. Its length is conventionally 2, 4, or 6 letters requiring low, moderate, and high amounts of short-term memory, respectively. Thus the target letters for comparing with each line of Fig. 5.2 might be HW (low level), OWPS (medium level), or QTXLDG (high level of short-term memory required). The time taken to complete the task would be measured.

Group 5: Tests stressing reasoning or some other form of central processing

A. Logical reasoning—1

The sequence 'AB' or 'BA' is given randomly. A statement about the sequence is given (that is, 'B does not follow A' or 'A precedes B'); the subject is required to answer if the statement is true or false. A test would consist of measuring how many examples could be done in 2 minutes.

B. Logical reasoning—2

A set of premises is given about the relationship between A, B, C, D, E (e.g. A > B; B = C; C > D; D = E). It is required to know what the relationship is between A and E, choosing from: greater than; less than; equal to; cannot say. Again how many examples could be done in 2 minutes would be measured.

C. Syllogisms

Accepting the truth of two premises, one has to choose the most appropriate conclusion from a set of possibilities. For example:

● Premise one: no foods are poisons

● Premise two: some drugs are poisons

Therefore, choose the most appropriate possibility from:

1. No foods are drugs
2. Some drugs are not foods
3. Some poisons are not drugs
4. No drugs are foods

The number of syllogisms done in 2 minutes would constitute the test.

D. Mental arithmetic

Take the example $47 + 93 - 28 = ?$ This is as obvious as it is tedious! Clearly a great variety of difficulty could be introduced into the tests. Again, how many could be one in a set period of time would be measured.

The final two groups of tests cannot be illustrated.

Group 6: Measuring speeds of response (reaction time)

A. Simple reaction time

When a light is switched on (or a note is sounded) a button must be pressed as quickly as possible; the delay in doing this is measured. The time taken to do this, say, 10 times is measured.

B. Choice reaction time

A modification of A is for a choice of buttons to exist; the correct button must be pressed to extinguish the light or stop the sound. The time taken to extinguish a sequence of, say, 10 lights or sounds is taken.

Group 7: Vigilance tests

Due to the very nature of vigilance, the tests to measure it must take much longer than is required for the other tests above. A test session lasting 30 minutes or more is not unusual. The tests require the subject to indicate when a signal is abnormal or missed. Thus a stream of pulses lasting 1 second each and given at 10 second intervals could be the 'background' (they could be sound pulses or pulses on a screen, for example); the 'signal' being sought could be the absence of a pulse, one that was shorter or longer than the standard value or one that appeared too soon or too late. In addition, the size and frequency of the 'errors' could be varied. The percentage of 'signals' that is detected correctly is generally measured.

How useful are these tests?

A great advantage of these tests—one that was not found in 'real' tasks—is that sets of them can be made of equal difficulty.

Therefore, differences in performance of these tests do not reflect variation in the tests themselves. If the external conditions are standardized (temperature, lighting, comfort of the volunteer) the results reflect the mental performance of the individual. But the tests are susceptible to many factors that can distort the results. Each session normally consists of several types of test, together with a vigilance session of, say, 30 minutes. The total session might take up to one hour. This not only makes it unlikely that employers will allow many such sessions per day (and that is a disadvantage scientifically) but it also means that the tests, particularly by virtue of necessarily being repetitive, are boring for the subject. There is also the problem that performance testing is highly susceptible to personal distractions and even though the tests and conditions of testing can be standardized, the motivation of those taking them cannot. For example, in some of our own experiments we found that subjects like to accompany each testing session with music. Unfortunately, slow music and fast music altered how they performed the tests so music is now forbidden during testing sessions. Another problem is that the tests show practice effects; that is, for the first day or so of testing, subjects' performances improve greatly (and so mask any daily rhythms) as they are getting used to the tests and are developing their personal ways of tackling them. To counteract this problem, subjects are given sufficient practice tests before the experiment to ensure that this effect has worn off. All these difficulties must be taken into account when we interpret the results of tests of mental performance.

What do these tests tell us about mental performance?

In spite of all these difficulties, results have shown that the different types of performance measured by these tests display characteristic rhythms. Some typical examples are shown in Fig. 5.5. For obvious reasons, most tests have been performed only during the daytime.

With the exception of tests in Group 4, performance rises after

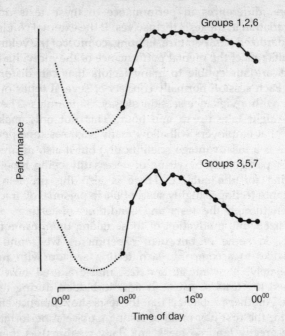

Fig. 5.5 Relationship between time of day (when awake) and performance at different group tests. Improved performances shown upwards. For meaning of groups, see p. 56. Dashed line indicates the kind of result to be expected if measurements were made during the night.

waking and falls during the evening. Between these times it shows either a slight rise or a general plateau (tests of Groups 1, 2 and 6) or a slight decline after a peak at about noon (Groups 3, 5 and 7). In most subjects there is also a temporary decline in the early hours of the afternoon—the 'post-lunch dip'. When subjects are tested at night their performance is generally rather poor. In short, the results of most tests are very similar to those measured 'on site', but with much more difficulty, see Fig. 5.1.

It will be noted that, in general, the performance rhythms are similar to those of temperature and adrenalin (see Chapters 1 and 4). One exception to this parallelism is those tasks which have a large short-term memory component (see Group 4 tests, above). These tasks appear to be done better at night with a general decline thoughout the daytime to lowest values in the early evening. A second exception to the parallelism between performance and temperature is a more general one. In stressful circumstances the effects of daily rhythms are 'swamped' by the response of the body to the emergency. For example, if you smell burning in the middle of the night you will respond immediately and fully, and not bother to 'consult' any body clock to see if you should calm down and be asleep! This applies to both your physical and mental performance. It is important, however, to remember that normally we are not stressed and so, particularly in repetitive and boring situations, the effect of our body clock upon mental performance becomes greater.

How well many tasks are performed is affected by another factor—'fatigue'. This is a mixture of tiredness and a kind of boredom and it produces a deterioration in mental performance. Fatigue increases and mental performance worsens as the amount of time spent on the task increases, particularly if we have lost sleep or the task is repetitive and boring. Vigilance (Group 7) is particularly susceptible to fatigue. To counteract this, an individual generally benefits from continual changes in the type of task being performed as well as continual updating on how well or badly the task is being done. There is also benefit to be gained from a break or—better—a short sleep. Fatigue contributes to the fall-off in performance that occurs as the time spent awake (or on duty) increases. This effect will be in addition to the daily changes in performance that are due to the body clock and which, therefore, would be predicted to peak between 4 and 6 o'clock in the afternoon. So, in tasks where the effects of fatigue are substantial (Groups 3, 5, and 7) peak performance will occur about noon rather than late in the afternoon (see Fig. 5.5).

Making the tests relevant to real tasks

Even though the rhythms in performance measured by the tests and 'real' tasks are similar (compare Figs. 5.1 and 5.5), it is reasonable to ask how relevant are these tests to the 'on site' situation? It seems possible to argue that the tests described so far—for example, crossing out duplicate letters from blocks of random letters, answering questions of logic relating to the sequence of two letters, and copying symbols—are tests produced by psychologists for use by psychologists and that their relevance to 'real' tasks remains to be proved. In attempts to deal with this type of criticism, the basic tests have been 'upgraded' in several ways. Examples are:

● Several types of test (and therefore several components of mental performance) have been combined. For example, in one test subjects are required to insert ball-bearings into holes in a cylinder; the holes are of slightly different sizes; the ball-bearings are of slightly different sizes; and the cylinder is revolving.

 Such a test combines elements of Groups 1–3. As another example, subjects have to draw an irregular shape—the shape being seen as a reflection in a mirror. This combines elements of Groups 1–3 and 5 with a fair degree of exasperation!

● Several tasks are required to be performed simultaneously and the subject is required to distribute his time between them as efficiently as possible. This is supposed to mimic the stress of the decision-making process. At times, it seems to those taking part to resemble a bad dream as they are required to be vigilant in spite of distractions elsewhere caused by other unfinished tasks!

● Complex computer-based games have been developed so that scores for manipulative skill, decision-taking, vigilance, etc. can all be calculated as the game proceeds. Clearly, games can be devised that are tests of far more subtle strategies and complex manoeuvres. Taken to an extreme, driving and flight simulators aim to duplicate the real thing exactly and if used repetitively they could assess changes due to daily rhythms.

Measuring mental performance by proxy

The use of sophisticated computer games and simulators certainly begins to mimic 'real' tasks—but we have reached another problem. The cost of buying equipment and the requirement of skilled personnel to maintain and run it can make its use in the repeated assessments which are required for measuring rhythms prohibitively expensive. We have almost come full circle. We have tried to measure 'on-site' performance of real tasks, but it was too complex and easily distorted. So we developed simple tests to overcome some of the difficulties, but they were often not very 'relevant'. So we made these tests more complex in order to increase their relevance, but in so doing we produced tests which were so sophisticated as not to be widely available due to cost and personnel requirements, and which began to show some of the problems found when we measured performance 'on-site'.

Is there an alternative to this at times unhappy compromise between 'relevance' and 'simplicity'? Some have suggested that there are daily rhythms which mirror those of mental performance but which are not as difficult to measure or as prone to interference, and they come up with old standbys, body temperature and adrenalin. The parallelism between these two rhythms and performance has been commented upon and illustrated before. That is, when performance in the field is difficult to measure satisfactorily, body temperature or adrenalin rhythms might be used as a substitute. But it must always be remembered that it is an assumption that body temperature and performance are parallel (or oppositely phased in the case of short-term memory), an assumption that has not been tested under all conditions, and so, at times, might be wrong. Nevertheless, it is a fact that during shiftwork and after time-zone transitions, body temperature and adrenalin rhythms have been used in addition to, or even in place of, measures of performance at 'real tasks' or at the simpler tests devised by psychologists.

Now try this—4

Measure your own performance

You might like to try and measure your own performance. This requires care and patience in the preparation, performance, and marking of the tests but it can be most rewarding. The comments are intended as guidelines only.

Choice of tests

With sufficient ingenuity all the tests except those in groups 2B, 3A, 5C could be devised by a computer. For many tests, they are best printed on paper, but for some, Groups 5–7, the test can be run on the computer screen.

How many tests required?

At least 20 sessions, spread over several days, are required to remove the major effects of practice. The investigation itself requires the test sessions to be repeated as often as possible, say on 5 occasions at each test time, to reduce the effects of variability. So, if you plan to measure performance at 8 times of day, then 40 complete test sessions, in addition to the practice sessions, will be required.

Performing the tests

Remember that performance is susceptible to the effects of external conditions, the mood of the subject and sleep loss, as well as to rhythmic changes. So it is most important to standardize your own frame of mind and the conditions for doing the tests.

Marking the tests

This has been described in the chapter. Generally, the rate of performance (that is, sums done in the time allotted or the time taken to complete the task) is scored rather than its accuracy. Note that a good performance is more sums done but less time taken. Individuals can differ widely in their scores and this makes direct comparisons between them difficult. One way to deal with this is to express each result from an individual as a percentage of the mean value for that person; in this way, all vary about the same mean value of 100 per cent. However, if you are looking for rhythmic changes in a single volunteer then it is the *changes* in performance, not the absolute level of performance, that are most important. Beware also of another problem. If you are scoring the tests yourself, rather than getting the computer to do it for you, then always do so at the same time of day—otherwise there would be variability due to time-of-day effects upon your scoring ability.

Good luck!

Lunch Time!

6

Your body clock and dealing with food

Another group of linked rhythms is that which includes rhythms in the intake and digestion of food, the chemical changes that are performed upon this food and the removal of waste material from the body.

Is it time to eat yet?

We do not eat throughout the 24 hours but show a rhythm that is dominated by social factors and the structure of our day. For example, coffee breaks, tea breaks, and a lunch hour are all incorporated into our work hours. Meal times can serve as a focus for certain social activities; consider, for example, the 'Sunday roast', the wining-and-dining of lovers, and even the 'working breakfast'. Fluid intake too, in the form of wine, beer, spirits, and a cup of tea, serves a social role as much as a biological one. Unlike babies, we do not eat or drink just because we are hungry or thirsty.

Many people, particularly night-workers, feel that they lose their appetite in the middle of the night. Yet it is not uncommon for people who cannot get to sleep, or who have woken up, to get up in the middle of the night and to make themselves a snack because they are hungry. On other occasions when people feel tired, and again this applies particularly to night-workers, they know they should eat (a rumbling stomach and hunger pangs tell them this) and yet have no appetite. Jaded palates need some titillation and yet another 'fry-up' might not be the answer. Clearly there is a complex mixture of physiology and psychology in this situation.

In many experiments upon individuals isolated from the time-cues in the environment (free-running experiments), food intake—breakfast, 'elevenses', lunch, etc.—continues to be distributed normally during the course of the waking span. Even though biological factors such as the state of hydration of the body will indicate that some food or fluid intake is required, the size and type of meal are likely to be determined also by habit and life-style. Having decided upon getting up, an individual will then eat several meals and snacks as part of a 'normal' pattern of eating. As in a normal environment, an individual in a time-free experiment will show a very similar pattern of eating day by day.

Even so, considerable differences between individuals and cultures exist. Some people miss breakfast, while others have their main meal at midday rather than the early evening. Interestingly, in those subjects living for fairly long periods in isolation, in whom the pattern of sleep and activity becomes irregular (see Chapter 2), meals too become erratic in their numbers and composition. Perhaps the loss of social interaction that is normally associated with mealtimes contributes to this.

Accepting that meals are a very important part of a person's life-style means that their timing might have an important role in adjusting the body clock. The effect can be direct, through the influence of food intake on gut activity (see below), or indirect, through the social factors that are associated with meals.

Indigestion and constipation

After eating the meal, the food must now be digested. This requires the co-ordinated release into our gut of a series of digestive enzymes and fluids which are then mixed with the food. The digested material is slowly passed through the gut by muscle action, and foodstuffs, water and salts are absorbed into our blood stream. What remains is converted into solid material for elimination as faeces.

There is no good evidence to indicate that these processes cannot be achieved by the body equally well at any time of the day or night. Our personal experiences—for example of the unpleasant effects upon our digestive system of an unusually large meal late at night—are difficult to interpret. In this case, was it the timing of the meal (the point in question), its size or richness, the wine, or the act of staying up late that was the cause? There is some evidence that the concentration of acid in the stomach is highest in the night and this might explain why the pain associated with excess gastric acid is most marked at night and can wake you then.

As food is taken into the gut, so there is a controlled sequence by which the gut contents are passed towards the anus. Once the residue left after absorption of foodstuff reaches the last part of the gut, the desire to defecate results. In herbivores particularly, but also in most animals and babies, defecation takes place more than once per day. In health, constipation is rare, being a reflection in many human cases of a lack of roughage in the diet. In adults, the decision whether or not to defecate is under voluntary control. Most of us defecate once a day and at a convenient time. When this routine becomes disorganised—as after time-zone transitions and during night-work—this can be inconvenient, particularly if we have a busy and highly-ordered life-style, and even socially embarrassing. When there are no social restraints, as in time-free isolation experiments, for instance, defecation appears to be more 'spontaneous'—that is, less regular and sometimes more frequent. The relative importance of habit and biological factors in such circumstances is hard to decide.

Making use of our food

The biological aim of the meal has been to enable foodstuffs to be taken into the body for its growth and repair. Fats are passed to fat storage depots and sugars to the liver and muscles. Several hormones, particularly insulin, the hormone that is deficient in sugar diabetes, control these processes. Insulin prevents the rise in blood sugar which would adversely affect brain function and cause sugar to be wasted by spilling over into the urine. The amount of insulin released into the bloodstream by the pancreas in response to eating a standard amount of glucose is less in the afternoon and evening than in the morning, and this suggests that there is a rhythm in the sensitivity of the pancreas to raised blood glucose. In addition the insulin appears to be slightly more effective in the morning at promoting glucose uptake and use by the cells of the body. Thus, the body appears to be able to respond more to raised blood glucose early in the daytime and this is in spite of the fact that we normally take in larger amounts of glucose later in the daytime.

Another difference between the effects of a morning and evening meal of equal size and calorie content has been found. Subjects tended to lose weight when they had breakfast only, but not when dinner was their only meal. Before a successful method for dieting is assumed to have been found it must be realized that the effects were small and that the difference might reflect the greater energy expended by those who ate in the morning. They had been 'set up' for the day by their large breakfast and so might have been more active than those who were hungry during the daytime. In other words, to be hungry throughout most of the day might cause lethargy and sluggish behaviour.

Recent work suggests that there might be a daily rhythm in the composition of a mother's milk. Particularly in countries where the diet is poor it might be of very considerable significance if the mother can make better milk at some times of the day. There is still, however, disagreement between researchers as to when the mother produces the most nutritious milk. This might reflect cultural differences as well as effects due to the type and quantity of food consumed by the mother. Further work remains to be done.

Our rhythmic kidneys

Linked to the intake and use of food and drink is the elimination in the urine of excess fluid and salts and of waste materials. Nearly all substances that appear in the urine show daily rhythms and these are due to our habits as well as our body clock. The internal cause of the rhythm can be established in the normal manner—by making the intake of food and water, the posture, and environment of the volunteers constant throught the 24 hours (see Fig. 1.3) The rhythm that persists in these circumstances indicates that the effect of the body clock and the difference from the normal rhythm is due to external causes. This type of experiment indicates that the relative importances of the external and internal causes depends upon the substance being considered. For example, the internal cause of the rhythm in potassium excretion is quite large, whereas for calcium and water excretion the external cause is dominant (see Fig. 1.3). Unfortunately, even if we know that a urinary rhythm is due partly to the body clock, we cannot yet be confident about details of the way in which this clock produces the rhythms in renal elimination.

The external cause of the rhythms of urine formation comes from two sources: our diet and changes in posture. The effects of meals are easy to understand. We drink and eat in the daytime but not at night and so there is an excess of fluid and salts in the body in the daytime, and a deficit during the night. Even so, the effects of posture (lying down when asleep and being more upright during the daytime) pose a problem. Lying down increases the return of blood back to the heart and brain. (It is for this reason that lying down when you feel faint is a good idea). Such an increased return of blood is monitored by receptors that signal the amount of filling of the heart. These receptors wrongly interpret the increased return of blood when lying down as a sign that excess blood volume has caused the blood vessels to become 'overfull' and so the kidney is instructed to remove the excess water and salts. (Such a reflex effect occurs also in outer space in a zero-gravity environment because blood no longer pools in the limbs then. The reflex increase in urine flow that is produced in this circumstance severely tested the resources of the space-suits worn by the early astronauts!) The problem is this: why is the reflex increase in urine flow so much smaller at night when we lie down to go to sleep? The answer is that renal function, like bodily functions in general, is highest during the daytime and partially 'closed down' at night. In the case of kidneys, this is brought about by several factors—by changed rates of secretion of some hormones (see Fig. 3.2), by altered activity in the nerves going to the kidney, and by a reduction in blood supply to the kidneys. It is a very good example of the internal cause of renal rhythms—the body clock—overriding the external cause, a change in posture. The result is important since it decreases the rate of bladder filling during the night and allows us to sleep longer. In daytime sleep, such an effect is not present and night-workers can vouch for the broken sleep produced by the more rapid filling of the bladder after lying down during the daytime. The effect is not observed in some renal and heart disorders; then the rate of urine flow on lying down at night is greater than during the daytime and this will be diagnostically useful to the physician. In babies and some old people also, renal rhythms are abnormal and the reduced urine flow at night is not seen. Particularly for old people this, coupled with a tendency to have a 'weak bladder', can have distressing consequences.

A knowledge of the rhythms in urine formation can be important when treatment with drugs is concerned since they are removed from the body in the urine. The degree of acidity of the urine shows a daily variation, nocturnal urine being most acidic. Many drugs are acidic or alkaline and this affects their removal in the urine; acidic drugs are excreted more easily in the daytime and alkaline ones at night. Since drugs are costly, it might be desirable to give the drug when it is less readily removed by the kidneys. This will reduce the amount of drug required and so the cost of treatment.

Giving less drug might have another advantage, since drugs are toxic materials and there is always the risk that the kidneys will suffer damage. Since the kidneys produce the largest volume of urine in the middle of the day, any drug that is being removed will be least concentrated in the urine, and so be least likely to cause damage, at this time.

It can be seen that the physician or doctor will have to bear both factors in mind when deciding if the time when a drug is to be taken is important (see also Chapter 14).

7

Your body clock at different stages of your life

We have considered so far daily rhythms in healthy adults. Here we will consider the differences from adults that are found in the rhythms of healthy babies, adolescents, and aged people. These are important times of our lives—too often biology books neglect them and assume we are forever in our youth and prime. Not only does the body clock contribute to the changes that are found, but also we can gain clues about the nature of it by a study of the changes.

The development of rhythms in young children

The newborn child does not show 24-hour rhythms, as any parent will affirm (Fig. 7.1). The baby's feeding habits, which directly concern a nursing mother, and its waking and crying habits, which directly concern both parents, tend to be distributed

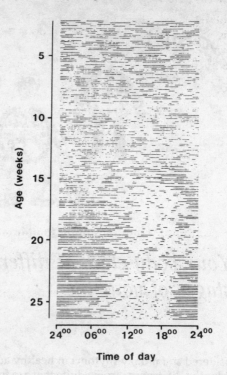

Fig. 7.1 The distribution of sleep (black bars) and wakefulness in one infant. Note that daily rhythms are absent or weak for the first 8 weeks and then show a period greater than 24 hours between 9 and 17 weeks.

evenly throughout the 24 hours (see the sleep profile of a newborn child in Fig. 2.4). As the baby grows up, 24-hour rhythms begin to appear from about the second month of life onwards. Fully established daily rhythms—that is, ones like those in adults—do not develop until about five years of age. Interestingly, not all rhythms develop at the same rate. As a general rule, those with the highest internal cause (body temperature, for example) develop later in life than those with marked external causes (urine flow, for instance).

The rhythm of sleep and activity is one of the first to develop. Why this should be so will be discussed in a moment but it does enable the other observations to be accounted for by a single theory. This theory is that, as in the adult, the changes associated with being asleep and awake will have a direct effect upon all rhythms, and so become the external cause of them. As a result of this, rhythms with the greater external cause will appear to develop earlier in childhood than those with a smaller external cause. This theory also implies that the internal body clock takes up to five years to develop fully. What causes the sleep/wake rhythm to arise first, and how does the body clock develop later?

External and internal causes for developing rhythms

The simplest answer to the question about what causes the sleep/wake rhythm to arise is that it is a reflection of the rhythmic world in which the newborn child has been placed and to which it begins to respond. Even if the baby wakes at random times—in order to feed, for example—there are some times of the 24 hours when its environment is less stimulating and responsive than others. This might be by parental design or due to natural events. Thus parents might decide to get the baby into a routine and this would mean imposing some sort of 24-hour cycle upon the child. This might include the amount of light, noise and general stimulation the child received during the daytime and the lack of these at night. It might also involve feeding times; during the daytime, meals would be given more readily in response to the child's cries than during the night. Even if the child were 'demand fed', its environment and parents' sleep would tend to decrease the likelihood of its waking and being fed at night in comparison with the daytime.

Accepting that the rhythms of children in a structured environmment appear to develop more quickly, is this advantageous to the child? In one study, body weight as well as general development progressed more in a group of premature babies living in a hospital nursery which imposed light/dark and noise/quiet rhythms than in a group who had been in a ward with less emphasis on the differences between night and day. Perhaps, therefore, a 'natural' rhythmic environment is beneficial.

It would be wrong to believe that the body clock develops only in response to a rhythmic environment and the effect upon the sleep/wake and feeding rhythms that this produces. There are several pieces of evidence that suggest that daily rhythms develop spontaneously even in the absence of environmental cues.

● In some children studied in a normal, rhythmic environment the sleep/wake rhythm shows an intermediate stage between a lack of rhythmicity and the presence of normal rhythms (Fig. 7.1). This intermediate stage consists of what appears to be a free-running rhythm with a period that differs from 24 hours. The observation that the period of the sleep/wake rhythm differs from 24 hours is important because it indicates that environmental cues cannot have been responsible.

● In rare instances, new-born babies have been studied for several months in a constant environment in a hospital ward. They develop a weak sleep/wake rhythm in the absence of external time cues, the implication of which has just been discussed.

● In rodents, rhythms continue to develop in animals that have been reared for several generations in constant conditions. This indicates that a rhythmic environment is not needed, but a possible effect from the rhythmic social and suckling influences of the mother has not been excluded.

● In fruit-flies—an insect much used by geneticists—and in rodents there are various mutants that show abnormal rhythmic behaviour. Some show no daily rhythms, others have a clock that runs faster than normal, with a 'daily' rhythm of 20 hours, and others show periods that are closer to 30 hours. These mutations can be transmitted from one generation to the next in breeding studies. Since these results are obtained in animals that have been living in a normal environment, they mean that the clock originates, at least in these animals, from an abnormal 'internal' structure, the chromosome.

But we would be equally wrong if we believed that the development of rhythms depended wholly upon internal factors.

It is probable that an individual's daily rhythms would not develop fully in the absence of a rhythmic environment. As with many other aspects of development, it is likely to be some mixture of 'nature and nurture'. The potential to develop normal rhythms is present in us all and is part of our genetic make-up. In normal environments this potential is fully realized. In environments in which there is little daily rhythmicity, the development of daily rhythms occurs (see above) but it is not quite normal insofar as the amplitudes (sizes) of the rhythms are likely to be less. In summary, with their development in infancy as well as their manifestation in adults, rhythms are associated with both external and internal causes.

Ultradian rhythms—the origin of daily rhythms?

It must not be assumed that the absence of a 24-hour rhythm in newborn babies means that they have no rhythms at all. Indeed, they do show rhythms in activity, waking, feeding requirements, bladder-emptying and body temperature—rhythms that all have a period between one and four hours and so are called ultradian. These ultradian rhythms are present in adults also, even though their amplitude is less than that of the 24-hour rhythm. The clearest example of this is the alternation of two types of sleep—dream sleep and deep sleep, as described in Chapter 3—but ultradian rhythms in urine production and the performance of mental tasks have been described also. We have already seen that it is common to feel tired about lunchtime (the 'post-lunch dip'); this is about 12 hours after retiring and so is another example of an ultradian rhythm with a period less than 24 hours.

It has been considered that the simultaneous presence of ultradian and daily rhythms suggests that they are related in some way and possibly all come from the same body clock. Further information about possible links can be obtained if we consider the way in which 24-hour rhythms 'grow' out of ultradian ones during infancy. Ultradian cycles do not lengthen to become equal to 24 hours. Instead, the times when one would expect the ultradian rhythm to produce a burst of activity or feeding drop out. Take as an example the feeding behaviour of a growing baby that is demand-fed. Initially he might be fed about every 4 hours. In due course the parents are relieved when he begins to 'miss' his two o'clock and then his six o'clock feeds. Presumably the 24-hour environment is interacting with his ultradian rhythms. At night, even though the baby has woken, the quiet, dark, unstimulating environment makes him more likely to go back to sleep. The important point is that if one ultradian peak is missed then the baby waits until the next peak. As infancy progresses, the ultradian peaks at night are missed as the effect of the *daily* (24-hour) rhythm becomes dominant.

In premature infants the development of the 24-hour sleep/ wake rhythm is delayed in comparison with that of full-term babies. This result might indicate that the body clock is slow to mature in premature babies. An alternative explanation, however, is that rhythms with a 24-hour period are received from the external world—but that these are picked up and transmitted to the body clock less effectively in premature babies. What is certain (see Chapter 14) is that the fetus can respond to inputs from its mother which show a 24-hour period, whereas the newborn baby—particularly when premature—is much less able to respond to 24-hour rhythms in this new environment. The time immediately after birth is one when the baby begins to respond to these new time-cues. The end result is that components with a 24-hour period are dominant, both in the environment and in the body clock, by the time the child has reached his fifth birthday.

In some children, the development of daily rhythms is poor. If the under-development applies to renal rhythms then the production of urine at night might be considerably higher than in normal children and this can lead to the problem of bed-wetting.

What all this work suggests is that the human's body clock and rhythms show several periods and that the combination of life-style and environment tends to accentuate one of these. Interestingly, a 12-hour day is regularly being practised in those countries where an afternoon siesta is taken, and also by those watch-keepers on merchant ships where the shift pattern of the officers is often 4 hours work followed by 8 hours leisure and sleep, the combination being undertaken twice each 24 hours. A sleep profile for someone on such a shift system is shown in Fig. 2.4.

Puberty and sexual maturation

The body clock plays a role in the complex changes that occur at puberty. Growth hormone is released into the blood during the first part of sleep, but this is affected by the 24-hour body clock to a small extent only, so that changes in the timing of sleep are followed almost immediately by changes in growth hormone release. However, growth hormone, like other hormones, is released in a series of short bursts and it is the frequency of these that is increased just after sleep onset (see Fig. 3.2). The total amount of growth hormone that is secreted per day increases to a maximum at about the time of puberty and is partially responsible for the growth spurt that is seen at about this time. During puberty, in addition to the frequent bursts of hormone release at night, there are smaller, less frequent bursts during the daytime. After puberty, the release of growth hormone tends to decline, first during the daytime and then during sleep; by old age (60 years and over) it has, in effect, fallen to zero, even at night.

These processes—a series of ultradian pulses, the frequency of which shows a 24-hour rhythm and the distribution of which alters with age—occur also with the sex hormones (see Fig 3.2). In the male, testosterone is secreted throughout the 24 hours with higher values at night. The total amount of testosterone secreted daily as well as the amplitude of the daily rhythm decline with age after a peak during youth; it resembles growth hormone, therefore, in these respects. For females, from puberty to menopause there is a monthly cycle of oestrogens and progesterone and, in these also, daily and ultradian rhythms of release are found. Such rhythms are normally observed throughout reproductive life, but the position is complicated because the amplitude of the 24-hour rhythm depends upon the stage of the monthly cycle that the female has reached. After menopause theses daily rhythms decline in amplitude towards zero.

Rhythms in old age

With increasing age, our daily rhythms begin to change. In general there are two types of change; a decrease in amplitude and an increase in the day-to-day differences in timing of the rhythm. Why should these changes occur?

One change that is associated with ageing and that will alter the rhythms of hormone release is the declining ability of the body to respond to instructions from the brain. This is very noticeable when the decreased amplitude of the daily rhythms of sex hormones is considered (see p. 81). Thus, at least initially, the decline of sexual function is because the ovaries or testes become less responsive to normal signals from the brain. In addition, ageing is associated with a general decrease in the ability of the body to respond or adjust to changes imposed upon it. Not only will this worsen the symptoms of 'jet-lag' and any problems associated with shift-work but also it impairs the effectiveness of many systems which are responsible for controlling the body. For example, the maintenance of blood pressure when changing from a lying to a standing position is achieved less rapidly as we age; as a result the blood supply to the brain is decreased for a longer time and there is a greater tendency to feel dizzy. Another example, with an all-too-frequent tragic outcome, is shown by temperature regulation. Older people are more susceptible to cold, in part because information from the brain in response to a lower blood temperature and a cool skin is acted upon less readily by the systems in the body that normally carry out those instructions.

There is the additional possibility that the body clock itself might, like other parts of the brain and body, deteriorate with age. The body clock has been studied very little in older volunteers and so we do not know the answer to this. Those few studies that have been carried out in free-running experiments suggest that the body clock might run slightly faster. As a result we will go to bed and get up earlier, and we become more like 'larks'.

It is possible that the strength of the daily clock also decreases in the aged; this would mean that the amplitude of the rhythms it influences would decrease. If this idea is applied to the sleep/ wake rhythm, it means that the 'polarity' between waking activities during the daytime and nocturnal sleep would decrease. Naps during the daytime and waking up during the night would both increase; these changes are often observed. There is, however, a possible external cause to them as well as, or instead of, the internal cause. Decreasing mobility and retirement are likely to reduce daytime activities and there will be a greater opportunity for daytime naps, particularly after lunch. Less sleep is needed by the elderly, but the habits of a lifetime might not be changed automatically, with the result that individuals retire earlier than necessary and too much time is spent in bed. Consequently, sleep might become disturbed, particularly when, in addition, kidney function does not decrease at night as much as it once did. All these factors—due to external and internal causes—will conspire to produce an individual who is less polarized in his life-style between day and night.

An increased freedom in life-style might be supposed to account for the increased variability in timing of daily rhythms that is found in the elderly. In a recent study performed by the authors, however, old people who lived at home were asked to record their habits each day (times of waking, eating, visiting friends, sleeping, etc) for a 'typical week'. In this way we could get some idea of the day-by-day variability in the subjects' habits. We found that older individuals showed less variability; in other words, they became more 'set in their ways' and this would tend to stabilize daily rhythms. Therefore, the day-by-day changes in the timing of rhythms seen in the aged do not appear to be due to day-by-day irregularities of habits, and this suggests an internal cause due to the body clock. Further, it is intuitively likely that a clock that is becoming less strong is also becoming less accurate.

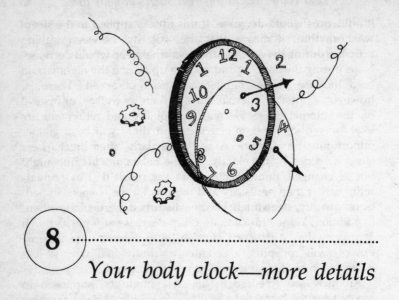

8

Your body clock—more details

We have discussed the evidence for a body clock and the kinds of rhythmic change that it normally produces. What we have not yet considered is where the body clock is and how it is adjusted by external time-cues. We then need to comment on the usefulness of such a clock.

Where is the body clock?

We do not know the exact site of the body clock in humans for the obvious reason that experiments to determine this are unethical. We do, however, have some fairly clear ideas as to its whereabouts in several mammals including monkeys, near-neighbours to us in an evolutionary sense.

Interest has centred on the role of two small groups of cells, one on either side of the brain, that are called the suprachiasmatic nuclei (SCN). Their position in the brain is important because:

- They are part of a region of the brain called the hypothalamus which also controls body temperature, food and water intake, sexual drive, and hormone secretion.

- They are close to those regions of the brain which are involved in controlling sleep and alertness and exchange large amounts of information with these areas.

- They are (as their name indicates) immediately above the optic chiasm, an area where the two nerves which carry visual information from the eyes cross over each other on their way to that part of the brain that analyses vision.

Evidence that the SCN are the body clock can be summarized as follow:

(1) Rhythmic electrical activity can be recorded from the nerve cells that make up the SCN and this rhythm has a period of about 24 hours. Clearly this is a promising start for a clock, but it might indicate instead that these cells receive a rhythmic input from another region of the brain which is the clock. In the same way, nerve cells in the spinal cord show activity whenever a particular movement is made by the arm. These cells are not, however, the *origin* of arm movement but are merely driven by other regions of the brain.

(2) Removing the SCN abolishes the rhythms of feeding, drinking, and activity. Although this result would be required if the SCN were the clock, two problems still remain. First, there would be the same result if the SCN were part of the transmission pathway by which the body clock communicates with the rest of the body (see above). Second, and this will be commented upon, some rhythms begin to show ultradian periods (that is, ones with a cycle length of 1–4 hours) rather than a complete absence of rhythmicity after removal of the SCN.

(3) Neural connections between the SCN and most other regions of the brain have been cut and yet the SCN has continued to be rhythmic. This appears to remove the objection raised in (1) above, except that:

- Severing *all* the inputs to the SCN is not possible technically.

- Chemical links between the SCN and the rest of the brain are not removed by this technique.

(4) Slices of the brain have been removed and incubated in special tissue-culture chambers. When these chambers have been maintained in constant conditions, the electrical activity from slices of the SCN, but not from other regions of the brain, has shown a daily rhythm.

(5) Very recently it has been shown that transplants of the SCN can be used to pass rhythmicity from one animal to another.

The results in (4) and (5) appear to remove the reservations expressed above. Do these findings, taken together, indicate that the SCN are the site of the body clock? Some would say they do, but others believe another interpretation is better. This alternative is based on the observations in (2) above that ultradian rhythms arise after removal of the SCN. They suggest that the SCN co-ordinates ultradian inputs (from other regions of the brain) to produce the 24-hour rhythm. Without the SCN the ultradian rhythms would continue—only the 24-hour component would be missing. Further work is required to test this idea. Certainly, if it were true, it would readily enable explanations for the simultaneous presence of daily and ultradian rhythms in the adult and the switch from ultradian to daily rhythms during the months after birth (see Chapter 7). The requirement for a clock to show more than one period is not a problem. Consider, for example, a mechanical clock: its several cogwheels will all turn at different rates and it is almost an arbitrary decision to link some of these to 'hands' that tell us the passage of the seconds, minutes, hours, or lunar month. So too with the body clock: it might be that several outputs with different periods are possible and that we tend to concentrate upon the daily or circadian clock because this is the period that is most useful to the organism and which has naturally been accentuated by the environment with its 24-hour period.

As far as humans are concerned, we know that SCN are present in that region of the brain which controls body temperature and the release of various hormones. It will be recalled that temperature and cortisol show a daily rhythm that is much influenced by the body clock and this suggests, but does not prove, that humans and other primates are very similar with regard to the site of the body clock.

How do time-cues exert their effects upon the body clock?

One advantage of siting the body clock in the SCN becomes apparent once we try to understand how time-cues might affect it. Considering the importance of the light/dark cycle as a time-cue, we must expect that there will be some sort of link between the body clock and the eyes. It has been shown in some animal species that there are nerves running from the eyes to the SCN. Whilst their presence does not prove that this is how the light/dark cycle normally adjusts the clock, it does seem to make it a very reasonable working hypothesis. To test this hypothesis further would require selectively cutting these nerves, which, as yet, has not been possible technically.

What about other time-cues? In humans, as we have shown, there are also possible time-cues from the timing of meals, the sleep/wake rhythm and social activities (see Chapter 2). Again, we do not know how the time-cues work but there are schemes that can very reasonably be suggested. Thus, sleeping and being awake are controlled by a region of the brain that is not only close to the SCN but also exchanges large amounts of information with them. In addition, activities—whether due to muscle exercise, mental effort, or the excitement associated with social interactions—will alter the amount of nervous activity passing through this region of the brain. Rhythmic changes in this neural activity could be the means by which an individual's lifestyle could act as a time-cue for his body clock. It is equally likely that the activities associated with meals (chewing, digesting and absorbing food) could all send information to the SCN via nerves from the gut. In addition, the absorption of food from the gut alters the relative concentrations of different amino acids (building blocks for protein) in the blood. This changes their uptake into the brain and incorporation into substances that enable brain cells to communicate with each other and the rest of the body. Clearly, a rhythm in food intake might be able to adjust the body clock via several mechanisms.

We stress that these are only proposals. They still require experimental evidence before they can be accepted as fact. Even so, we are taking the first steps in a long journey towards an understanding of the body clock and the way it adjusts to our environment.

The usefulness of the body clock

What advantage do we gain by possessing a body clock? Could we not argue that the plant or animal responds to the rhythms in its environment anyway? (That, after all, is what is meant by the external cause of a daily rhythm.) For example, could we not argue that the plant could move its leaves in response to the sun; the shore-dwelling creature leave its burrow in the mud when the tide recedes; or the diurnal or nocturnal animal respond to sunrise and sunset? Notice that by this argument, such changes are initiated from outside the organisms and so inevitably occur *after* the initiating event. Particularly with plants, these responses might be rather slow. For example, the process of moving leaves into the right position to catch most sunlight takes time, so that, because the sun appears to move continuously, the position of the leaves will always be behind the ideal one. For the animal in its mud burrow, valuable time will be lost if it cannot prepare itself for foraging until *after* the tide has left the shore. The advantage of a body clock is that it *can prepare an animal or plant and enable it to predict a future environmental condition and so be ready for the event when it takes place*. Thus the plant can, during the latter part of the night, move its leaves to a position appropriate for sunrise; predatory animals can prepare themselves for the activity of hunting and hunted animals can escape to safety before it is too late. For humans, as we have discussed in Chapter 1, the body has been 'waking us up' since about 5 o'clock in the morning so that, by the time we normally wake, we are prepared for the rigours of a new day; in the evening our body begins to 'tone us down' to prepare us for getting to sleep.

Responses to the environment are still required, of course, because the body clock is not a perfect timekeeper and, anyway, environments cannot be predicted precisely—the tide can be higher, food abnormally scarce, or the day more cloudy so darkness comes earlier. Both mechanisms—that due to the clock and that due to the environment—are required by a living organism, and our previous discussion of the roles of the environment, as an external cause of a rhythm as well as a *zeitgeber* giving time-cues to adjust the body clock, shows how intimate their combination is under normal circumstances.

This integration between the environment and the organism is a fine example of the evolutionary response of a living organism to ecological factors. Ecology is the study of the organism and its relationship to the environment. Time and rhythms are an integral part of this relationship. Humans are bounded by such principles as much as are other living organisms. Technological advances might mean that we live in an artificial environment with respect to time-cues, but it is a *rhythmic* environment nevertheless, and our possession of a body clock means that all the advantages that come from the integration of biological and environmental rhythms apply equally to ourselves.

Now try this—5

A scientific problem—number 1

To get some ideas of the difficulties involved in studying the body clock—a structure hidden inside the brain whose activity can only be inferred indirectly by measuring the rhythms it is believed to produce—consider the following analogy.

A family of four is believed to be involved in organizing a spy-ring from their home. You have to prove this. You have free access to the family outside their house, but when they are inside you can investigate them only by looking through the windows of their house. You have no helpers and can only devote a total of 4 hours observation time to the task on any day.

What is the best way to approach the task?

The answer will depend upon your definition of 'best', of course, but some of the decisions you will have to make are listed below. (Comments in brackets refer to comparable diffi- culties when studying the body clock.)

(1) When should you study the family? (You are rarely able to sample rhythms as often as you would like.)

(*a*) Are your 4 hours of observations made in a single session or a number of sessions?

(*b*) If it is a single session, is this at the same time or at different times each day?

(*c*) If it is at different times, then how do you arrange them?

(*d*) If it is a number of sessions, then how many? Having decided upon this you then have the problems in (c).

(2) How should you study the family when it is at home? (Do you concentrate on a large or small area of the brain; if the latter, which one, if the site of the clock has not been established beyond all doubt?)

(*a*) Do you follow one person only throughout your observation time(s) or choose, instead, a single place to see which of the family, if any, are there?

(*b*) If you choose to observe a single place, then do you study a place that is large or small, say, the front garden, a single- room, or the exit at the end of the drive?

(*c*) If it is a single room, which one? Do you change the room? If so, how often? To which other place?

You might argue that such an investigation, though time- consuming, would enable you to build up the picture you want. But consider how the following additional constraints would make your task so much more difficult (and relate these constraints to the problems of being unable to study the SCN directly, of being unsure of exactly how it then sends its information to produce the rhythms in, say, temperature or urine flow—things that we *can* measure—and even of not being certain that the SCN is the only area in the brain that is part of the body clock).

1. You are not quite sure exactly how the spies would communicate with each other—that is, are you to investigate letters, phone calls, radio transmissions, or informal notes?

2. The house is surrounded by a high wall. You know that there are many paths leading to the house and from the house, *but*:

(*a*) You do not know how many there are, where they come from, or where they go to.

(*b*) You cannot study some of these paths closely—they are guarded and can be viewed only from a distance.

(*c*) In addition, there are so many visitors that you have no time to question them all. Which would you choose?

(3) There is now a rumour that the family has another house, which may be used for organizing the syndicate, in addition to/ instead of the house you are observing, but you don't know the location of the other house.

It is not quite so simple now, is it? Even though you might continue to build up a picture of the whole operation, it must be based upon an increasing number of assumptions—and assumptions might be wrong, with potentially catastrophic effects upon the correctness of your account of the family and its activities.

Part II

Your body clock in disorder

We have considered so far the daily rhythms of humans in health. In Part II we describe the effects of abnormalities of daily rhythms. These abnormalities arise either because there is an abnormality in some aspect of the timing system itself or because modern society has made demands upon us that have outstripped our biological evolution. But to end our book on jet-lag and shift-work would be too negative, and so we will end by describing an area in which the knowledge of daily rhythms has enabled a small but important contribution to medicine to be made—the diagnosis and treatment of illness and disease.

9

Abnormalities and daily rhythms

In the simplest terms, the daily timing system consists of a body clock that is synchronized by external time-cues and that sends information to a variety of systems in the body and so produces daily rhythms in them. Intuitively, one would guess that abnormalities could arise at many points in such a system and we will now consider severe clinical disorders which bear this out.

Patients with severe illness and general irregularities in daily rhythm

Daily rhythms are abnormal in subjects who have recently undergone major surgery or who are in intensive care because of serious illness. There are many reasons why this might be so. Some possibilities are:

- The patient, particularly in an intensive care unit which has artificial rather than natural lighting, is in an environment that is poor with respect to natural time-cues.

- The patient's treatment—including artificial feeding, ventilation, etc.—is likely to be continuous rather than rhythmic. Many drugs will be given if and when needed, probably with no obvious rhythm.

- The patient's perception of his environment and his response to it is likely to be grossly reduced, since he might be unconscious or paralysed, for example.

Accepting these abnormalities in the patient then the abnormality of the timing system that might be observed could take one of several forms. There could be:

- A complete loss of rhythmicity (because the body clock or its expression has been suppressed);

- A free-running rhythm with a period greater than 24 hours (because the time-cues were too weak or the subject was unable to receive or respond to them adequately);

- A rhythm of reduced amplitude (because the external cause of a rhythm was reduced and/or because the internal cause was weak);

- An abnormal clock period due to recurrent episodes of an illness or its treatment.

Bearing all these factors in mind, the demonstration that patients in intensive care show abnormal daily rhythms, and that these abnormalities take on many forms, is not surprising. Unfortunately, since there are so many possible explanations, the correct one is most difficult to ascertain. Yet, if a lack of time-cues or a difficulty in perceiving them were important in some cases, then a possibility that has not yet been tested is one of attempting to promote the presence of 24-hour rhythms in a patient by increasing external time-cues or by administering sedation and intravenous feeding on a daily schedule. The basis for such a treatment would have some parallel with the imposition of a daily routine and 24-hour environmental cues upon premature babies (see Chapter 7).

A loss of adjustment to the 24-hour day

Some individuals, even when living in normal society, do not remain in synchrony with the 24-hour day and instead free-run with a period of about 25 hours. For some, the reason is one of choice; they do not have a job or social links that tie them to a 24-hour day. A single, introverted individual who was self-catering and whose job did not require contact with others would be able to live like this. There is not necessarily any 'problem' here. Such an individual could choose to ignore conventional time-cues and so cocoon himself in an artificial world in which meals and artificial lighting are adjusted to accord with the dictates of his body clock—like the subject in a cave (in chapter 2) and the opposite of what happens normally, when our life-style adjusts our body clock. His sleep pattern might look something like that shown in Fig. 2.2.

There are, however, some examples where the individual appears unable to adjust to a 24-hour routine in spite of attempts to do so. One example was of a graduate who enjoyed a good job with normal daytime hours. His body clock free-ran so that on occasions he was the victim of a clash between an internal cause—which thought it was night and wanted him to sleep—and an external cause, society—which required him to work in the (real) daytime. The unfortunate subject would feel tired at work and yet have difficulty in sleeping at night. At other times, the demands of his body clock and society coincided but then much of his time would be spent catching up on lost sleep. In fact this individual found the stress of such an existence too much and was forced to leave his job.

Less extreme cases than this are more common (see Fig. 2.4). Thus individuals might retire and rise progressively later each day until they would miss a whole sleep because it was going to clash with daytime commitments. At this point they would go to bed slightly earlier than the rest of us (because they were tired), and start the delaying process all over again. The problem seems to be that social factors are not a strong enough time-cue. This might reflect the individual's lack of interest in normal social factors, some error in the pathway linking time-cues to the body clock or some abnormality in the clock itself—an insensitivity to normal time-cues, for example.

There is another group, the blind or partially sighted, who cannot make satisfactory use of the light/dark cycle as a time-cue. Even though their life-style is often timed normally, daily rhythms of body temperature and the concentrations of the hormones melatonin (see below) and cortisol in the blood are irregular, often with what appears to be a free-running period. Even though the obvious explanation of the abnormal rhythmicity is that these people suffer from the loss of the light/dark cycle as a time-cue, the result also indicates that the other time-cues (social factors, activity, and mealtimes) are inadequate.

Promoting adjustment to a 24-hour day

For those examples that have been described so far, the best advice that can be given to individuals is to help them to strengthen their time-cues and to take more notice of them. (Readers might be reminded of Now Try This—2, Chapter 2). For example, an individual with difficulty in adjusting to a 24-hour day should make every attempt to strengthen the rhythmic influence of social factors and meal times by adhering as rigidly as possible to a regular routine. In addition, he might consider taking a shower or some exercise on waking, procedures which are aimed at stressing a regular start to the day.

Another method that has been tested upon some blind people is the regular use of the hormone melatonin, a product of the pineal gland. The pineal gland is a small structure buried deep on the brain. Its function in man is not certain. (It was believed by Descartes to be the seat of the soul.) In some animals its biological role is more clearly defined. In them it is concerned with picking up information about the timing and length of daylight. This information is then used to control the seasonal breeding cycle. Since the pineal produces its hormone melatonin only during the dark, melatonin might also be used to match the sleep/wake rhythm of the animal to the light/dark rhythm. In such cases melatonin might be some sort of 'darkness indicator' and some have even called it an 'internal time-cue'. The important point is that melatonin might be a link between the environment and body clock in ourselves also and its release might promote inactivity or tiredness. There is some support for this in that melatonin capsules can be taken in the evening to produce a consistent overnight rise in the blood concentration of this hormone and that this treatment appears to stabilize the sleep/wake rhythm of blind subjects.

Clocks adjusted to the wrong time—'Monday morning blues' and some forms of insomnia

Most of us experience 'Monday morning blues'—the feeling of tiredness and low spirits on the first day back at work after the weekend of rest. Our body clock has adjusted readily enough to the delay in our life-style at the weekend (remember that the free-running period is more than 24 hours), but is less easily advanced, as is required, on Sunday night and Monday morning (see Chapter 2). Most of us are back to normal by Tuesday, however, because we can advance our body clock, even if with some difficulty.

Insomnia is a common complaint in which the sufferer has poor sleep that is often broken many times during the course of the night. There is no evidence in the great majority of cases that an altered body clock is in any way responsible, but there is one group of people who suffer from a fairly rare form of insomnia called Delayed Sleep Phase Syndrome. They cannot get to sleep until about 2 o'clock in the morning or later, even when they go to bed much earlier. As a result, they are normally very tired during weekdays when they are compelled to wake at a normal time for work. On holiday and at weekends, however, they recover their loss of sleep since they can get their full quota, say 8 hours, between 2 and 10 o'clock in the morning. They are not free-running—they are stabilized to a 24-hour day. It is just that they show a very late timing of their sleep/wake rhythm with respect to normal time-cues. It appears that they can delay their body clock with ease but they cannot advance it, so that if they ever go to bed late then they are stuck with a body clock (and bed-time) that tends to become ever more delayed.

The treatment is simple.

- Patients are asked to go to bed 3 hours later each 'night' and get up 3 hours later each 'morning'—this they will find easy, of course.

- After several days on this schedule they will be going to bed and getting up at their chosen time, one that gives them enough sleep during the weekdays.

- They must now stick strictly to a 24-hour life-style—no late nights—or they will have to begin treatment all over again.

This is not a cure, since the underlying problem has not been tackled. Indeed, the exact cause of the problem is not clear, though possible explanations include:

- A body clock that runs slower than average;
- Poorly developed means by which time-cues are passed to the clock;
- A body clock that is insensitive to normal time-cues.

Whatever the explanation, the above treatment is cheap, does not involve drugs and gives the patient a greater control over his treatment.

An even less common form of insomnia is Advanced Sleep Phase Syndrome. When one considers the symptoms (going to sleep and waking up very early), the treatment (advancing the patient's life-style by 3 hour per 'day' until it is correctly timed), or the possible causes (a clock that runs faster than average), it is seen as the opposite of Delayed Sleep Phase Syndrome.

Perhaps it will have occurred to the reader that there might be links between the disorders and treatments described so far. Thus a free-running rhythm indicates that the time-cues are not strong enough to entrain the body clock to a 24-hour period. This might be because the time-cues are too weak, the transmission of them to the body clock is poor, the clock itself is insensitive to time cues, or it possesses an abnormally long or short free-running period. The treatment has been to strengthen the time-cues by increasing the regularity of an individual's life-style (and all the time-cues this entails), or by mimicking this by taking melatonin regularly. Further, as is often the case, the clinical conditions might be regarded as rather extreme cases of variability in the ease with which we adjust our body clock, a process that is found normally within the human population. As discussed in Chapter 7, ageing increases the tendency for us to become 'larks'—and some of us are 'larks' anyway—because the body clock has then a free-running period that is below the average for the population as a whole. In an extreme case, this might result in Advanced Sleep Phase Syndrome and even require clinical treatment. Likewise there might be a progressive increase in the free-running period of the body clock as we pass through the sequence: 'slightly an owl', 'definitely an owl', Delayed Sleep Phase Syndrome, free-running rhythm in normal society.

Some forms of depression—inadequate timing systems?

There are many forms of depression and a connection between abnormal body clocks and three types of depression have been suspected: rapidly cycling manic-depression, some forms of endogenous depression and seasonal affective disorder. At the outset we must state that the picture is still very unclear and that those forms of depressions which can be linked to an abnormal body clock are likely to form only a small proportion of all cases.

Manic depression

Patients with this disorder switch between mania and depression; a few do so regularly. One very clear example is shown in Fig. 9.1. Also included is a plot of the time of peak of body temperature on successive days. The time of peak becomes progressively earlier. When the temperature peak was at about the normal time, the patient showed a temporary remission of symptoms; when the temperature was timed too early she tended to feel depressed; and when it was timed too late she tended to experience mania. One explanation of the progressive advance of the temperature rhythm is that it is being driven by a body clock that is running too fast. In this case it shows a period of about 21 hours which is too rapid to be adjusted to a normal value of 24 hours.

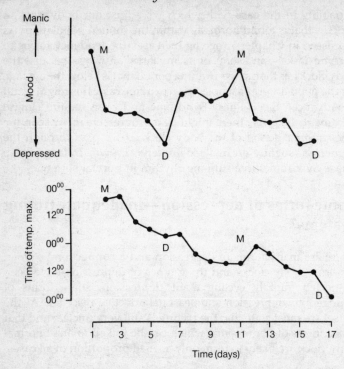

Fig. 9.1 Cyclic variations in self-assessment of mood (top) and times of peak of body temperature rhythm (bottom) in a manic depressive. Mood sometimes extreme enough to be classified clinically as mania, M, or depression, D.

Interestingly, some, but not all, patients ('lithium responders') show a remission of symptoms when they take tablets containing lithium salts. Lithium exerts many effects in the body. It has been shown that, in some animals, one of these is that lithium slows the free-running period of the body clock. The argument might be put forward, therefore, that the treatment slows the body clock enough for it now to be adjusted to a 24-hour day by normal time-cues. The 'explanation' raises many problems, not the least being why the symptoms should depend upon whether the temperature rhythm is delayed or advanced with respect to the sleep/wake rhythm.

Endogenous depression and seasonal affective disorder

In some cases of endogenous depression there was one symptom which suggested that an abnormality of the internal clock might exist. It was where depression was most marked in the morning and decreased during the course of the day. It was also noted that patients reported an improvement in their mood if they were woken early or deprived of sleep and so, presumably, exposed to daylight much earlier in the day. The idea arose that in healthy subjects there is a 'critical period' early in the morning (but after we have woken up) when light is 'required' by the body. In patients with this type of depression, their critical period is advanced so that it falls during sleep. As a result, the body would not normally receive light during the critical period, but it would do so if the patient stayed awake all night or got up early. In apparent agreement with this idea, some subjects appeared to benefit from continual advances of their sleep/wake rhythm (as though they were continually flying eastward) or by being woken temporarily at about four o'clock in the morning to receive a burst of bright light for about an hour. Both treatments would enable patients to be awake and so to receive light at their earlier 'critical period'. The advance of this criticial period, however, cannot easily be linked to the idea of a body clock which tends to run fast and so produce daily rhythms which are timed too early because, when daily rhythms have been investigated in these patients, it appears that daily rhythms are *irregular*, rather than altered in a particular direction.

There is, however, one type of depression in which shifts of daily rhythms are found more regularly—Seasonal Affective Disorder (SAD). Strictly, this is outside the remit of this book since it is a seasonal or annual rhythm, but we include it since it is believed to involve a disorder of daily rhythms. Seasonal affective disorder is associated with depression that is marked during the Winter and early Spring and regresses in the Summer. It has been suggested that it occurs when susceptible individuals do not get enough natural light during the winter months. In support of this view is the finding that the incidence of SAD amongst different populations increases as one passes from the equator towards higher latitudes—as do the length of the winter nights and the likelihood of waking in the dark on winter mornings. Early successes in the treatment of this disorder consisted of exposing patients to bright light in the morning, so mimicking the longer hours of daylight associated with summer. More recently, however, it has been found that bright light at other times of the day—in the evening, which also mimics the light in summer-time, and at noon, which does not lengthen daylight hours—has an effect also.

As we have already discussed, bright light acts as a time-cue in humans and so might be helping patients not only because it fell in a critical period (though how this might work is still not known), but in addition, or instead, because it adjusted the body clock and so removed a conflict of timing between the patient's body clock and his sleep/wake rhythm. Thus, if the body clock is delayed then one tries to advance it by giving bright light in the morning, and if it is advanced then the light is given in the evening to delay it. (In effect, such treatment is using bright light as a time-cue to adjust the body clock appropriately.) Some researchers have obtained very impressive results with such a treatment. Patients recover from their depression at about the same time that their body clock, as measured by the melatonin rhythm, adjusts its phase to match the sleep/wake rhythm. Whilst this is an effective treatment, there are certain comments that must be considered from a scientific viewpoint:

- Some patients should have bright light when it would be predicted to worsen their symptoms by adjusting the body clock in the wrong direction. Of course there are ethical problems here but, in the absence of these control experiments, it might be that light is exerting its effect by some other means, say, by encouraging the patient to become more active.

- How well do changes in the melatonin rhythm measure changes in the body clock? (Remember the hypothesis is that the treatment is successful because it adjusts the clock.) Adjustment of other markers of the body clock (such as body temperature) should also be measured.

- With all treatments that are designed to improve the mood or feelings of a patient, the placebo effect must also be considered. The placebo effect means that *any* treatment will improve a patient merely because he wants to recover and is responding to the clinician's attempts to help rather than to a specific treatment.

In summary, it is not yet clear that a modification of the daily rhythms is a necessary requirement of treatment or that an abnormality of the body clock is the cause of the disorder. It should also be pointed out that other circumstances where there is an abnormality of timing of the body clock (for example, after a time-zone transition, during shift-work, in blind subjects and in patients with Delayed Sleep Phase Syndrome) all tend to produce and feeling of malaise rather than a fully-blown clinical depression. Further work needs to be performed in this important area. For example, it is possible that clinical cases are only an extreme form of a normal reaction to the short winter days. It must be realized that many people are less excited about going to work in the dark rather than the light—a dull start to the day. Also it might be that those who suffer from SAD differ from most people only because they are more susceptible than the rest of the population to feeling 'under the weather' when they do not see daylight, particularly in the morning. If this is correct then there are important implications for people who are 'near the borderline', if it is decided not to change the clocks between the summer and winter, but rather to retain Daylight Saving Time throughout the year. The extra hour of daylight in the winter evenings that this would mean would also be accompanied by an extra hour of darkness in the winter mornings.

Now try this—8

A scientific problem—Number 2

Consider the following comments about SAD. Can you devise ways of testing them? These are questions designed to test an understanding of the scientific method, *not* means of diagnosis or recipes for treatment. (If you think that you are a SAD sufferer then contact your doctor.)

(1) Most SAD cases are referred to clinics in the months December to April.

(*a*) How could you test if the factor which causes SAD was lack of light or the cold weather?

(*b*) Would you get more information by considering patients who had suffered for several years rather than only once?

(2) Bright light is often found to bring relief.

How would you eliminate a placebo effect—that is, the treatment works because the patient thinks (or hopes) that it will?

(3) Carbohydrate (sugar) intake is found to increase in patients with SAD.

How could you show that this was *not* because chocolate bars, sweets, etc., are more likely to be eaten since your depression means that you cannot be bothered to cook a proper meal?

Some comments follow on the next page.

1. (*a*) Ask patients when the symptoms first appeared. (This assumes they can recall this accurately). Does this tend to correspond to spells of cold weather, to times of dull weather, or the the length of daylight? Does the onset of SAD symptoms depend upon whether the subject lives an 'outdoor' or 'indoor' life?

   (*b*) The patients could keep a diary of their moods throughout the year, a form of self-diagnosis. Moreover, they are likely to consult their doctor after a shorter delay if their SAD is a recurrent problem; this is a suggestion that could be tested statistically.

2. Give some other 'treatment' that does not involve bright light. Exercise? Sitting in front of a set of dim lights? Giving noise or music? Unfortunately, patients are likely to have learned from media coverage that light is somehow involved, so they will have a prejudice against other treatments. Even so, giving bright light at a time which should not affect the body clock or even adjust it in the wrong direction could be tested—as has already been described.

3. Make all types of food (protein, fat, and roughage as well as carbohydrate) equally easy to obtain. In practice this might require constant supervision of the patients over the course of several weeks. An alternative would be for patients to keep a daily record of their food. Not all could, or would, do this but, even if they did, the problem that patients might choose the type of food because of habit rather than careful deliberation still exists. (In fact, there is carbohydrate *craving*, so it is not just a matter of apathy about cooking.)

We hope another point is made by these questions and comments, namely that the problem is very complex, requires large amounts of meticulous study, and the results are most difficult to interpret unambiguously.

10

Time-zone transitions— the problem

What is jet-lag?

The tour operator for a trip to New York, Delhi, or any distant land will stress the comfort and the excitement of it all, the new places, people and life-style, and the sense of romance and adventure. The possible fatigue, indigestion, headaches, irregular bowel habits, difficulty with sleeping and concentrating—in fact, generally feeling 'below par'—will not be mentioned. These are the symptoms of 'jet-lag', and they are being experienced by more and more people as flights—many no longer a short journey across to France but spanning the globe—become more common.

How does jet-lag affect us? Why do we get it? And, most importantly, what can we do about it?

The symptoms of jet-lag have already been mentioned. They constitute an assortment of ill-defined symptoms that affect people in different ways and to different extents. Typically, a person suffering from jet-lag will feel tired at some point in the daytime and yet be unable to sleep well at night through difficulty getting to sleep or waking early. This will increase a sense of general fatigue and might result in headaches and difficulties with concentration. Appetite might be poor and food that is eaten will be difficult to digest; bowel movements will occur at inconvenient times in the night or at unaccustomed times during the day, or the traveller might suffer constipation for a few days. Older people, those who are less regular in their life-style and solitary people, all tend to be affected more than the young, the methodical and the social extrovert. The symptoms are generally worse the further you fly and they are more marked after eastward flights than those to the west. Flights in a north–south direction (or vice versa) give less trouble than either eastward or westward journeys.

What causes jet-lag?

Why is the body so disorientated? There is a combination of two factors: the change in time zone and the sluggishness of our body rhythms to adjust to change. We must consider each in turn.

Time zones

The Earth revolves on its axis once every 24 hours. As a result, each country (except those close to the Poles) will experience sunrise, the passage of the sun across the sky, sunset and night once each revolution. Because of the direction in which the Earth revolves, the sun always rises in the east and sets in the west. As we travel to the east, therefore, these events occur earlier and, on a westward journey, they take place progressively later. The time at which the sun is highest in the sky is also affected in the same way. This moment is defined as noon on local time. This has the obvious advantage that all countries match their local time to the hours of daylight, but it also means that different countries have different local times.

In order to standardize all these local times, the worlds has been divided into 24 time zones—each spanning 15° longitude. Matters are made easier for us in the United Kingdom since the

time zone that all others are related to is that which passes
through England—Greenwich Mean Time (GMT). Countries to
the east of us are in time zones with local time that is ahead of
GMT, whereas local time and the time zones to the west are
delayed with respect to ours. For example, when it is 4 o'clock in
the afternoon (1600)—in England, it is 11 o'clock in the morning
(1100) in New York (5 time zones to the west), 8 o'clock in the
morning (0800) in Los Angeles (8 time zones to the west),
8 o'clock in the evening (2000) in Abu Dhabi (4 time zones to the
east), and midnight (at the end of the day) in Singapore (8 time
zones to the east). The position is complicated in 2 ways. First,
countries modify local time by 1 or 2 hours, according to whether
it is winter or summer, in order to make more use of the daylight
hours. Second, if a traveller goes eastwards halfway round the
Earth he will have passed through 12 time zones and gained 12
hours with respect to GMT; he will meet another traveller who
has travelled westward and so is 12 time zones (12 hours) behind
GMT. At this point on the Earth (180° longitude) the International
Dateline is reached. Suppose it is 12 noon on a Monday by GMT;
at this moment, to the traveller who has travelled eastwards it
will be midnight at the end of Monday, but to the westward
traveller it will be midnight at the beginning of Monday. That is,
crossing the International Date Line means that we either gain a
day (eastwards crossing) or lose one (westwards crossing).

A further consequence of having time zones is that, when we
travel we have to adjust to local time in the new time zone. It is
this adjustment which causes difficulties for our body rhythms.

The body clock and time-zone transitions

The advantage of our body clock is that it improves the way in
which we fit into a rhythmic environment (this was considered
in more detail in Chapter 8). Thus our falling plasma adrenalin
and body temperature in the evening prepare us for sleep by
toning us down, just as rising values from 5 o'clock in the
morning onwards prepare us for the rigours of a new day. An
important property of such a clock is its stability; that is, its
timing does not alter much from day to day.

It can be seen that this very advantage now becomes
disadvantageous after a time-zone transition when an adjustment

of our body to new local time is required. For some days after the flight, the body clock—and with it our daily rhythms—will tend to lag behind. Not only do we feel disorientated with respect to our habits but also there are more objective measurements to indicate that the flight has disorganized us. If we measure our rhythms in mental performance (our ability to do mental arithmetic or to reason logically) we find that the normal daytime peak, with a morning rise and evening fall, is absent. Instead, we might find that performance is improving just before bedtime, and deteriorating after sleep. Superimposed upon this will be a general decline in performance due to loss of sleep and fatigue. Moreover, body temperature and adrenalin rhythms will show a similar disorientation.

'Jet-lag' is the consequence of there being a mis-match between our body clock and the external timing, because our body clock is slow to adjust to the change in local time. Knowledge of this fact, together with understanding some properties of our body clock, will enable us to promote adjustment of our clock to the new time zone and so reduce the difficulties of jet-lag.

Other explanations of jet-lag

There is no reason whatsoever why our explanation of jet-lag as a consequence of a mismatching between the body clock and the new external environment should go unquestioned. Accordingly, we offer some comments on some alternative 'explanations' that have been given. As is often the case, they contain some truth and can be used constructively when attempting to deal with jet-lag.

It is 'in the mind'

This is partially true. Many of the symptoms of jet-lag relate to how we feel, but such an explanation does not explain why we should feel below par, and seems less acceptable when one would expect the mind to be concentrated on enjoying oneself on holiday or performing at one's peak on business or at athletics, for instance. Moreover, the abnormal timing of bowel habits, of hunger and, particularly, of temperature, performance, and hormone rhythms is difficult to explain in these psychosomatic terms. Certainly, expecting that you will suffer from jet-lag hardly helps and this becomes an argument for adopting a positive attitude to the difficulties and knowing that they can be minimized by following the advice we give later.

It is due to the inconvenience of intercontinental flight

Disruption of our normal routine, loss of sleep, waiting for the flight to be called, and the apprehension associated with flying will all take their toll. The severity of jet-lag, however, is dependent upon the number of time zones crossed rather than the length of flight. This is why jet-lag is not so marked after a flight in the north–south direction. To be sure, the general inconvenience of such a flight disrupts you and makes you tired, but only temporarily, so that there are no symptoms of jet-lag by the second day at your destination.

The effect of time-zone changes, free of problems from the flight itself, can be removed by experiments in isolation chambers. In these, the subjects live a normal routine by the clock and then, suddenly, the clock can be changed. For example, if might be 12 noon and the experimenter might change the clock to 8 o'clock in the evening, so mimicking a time-zone transition to Singapore. The subjects must continue to live their normal routines, but now in accord with the new local time. The inconvenience of flight has been removed; has jet-lag? In such simulated time-zone transition experiments, changes to the body's rhythms are observed to be very similar to those after real time-zone transitions. In addition, many components of jet-lag— altered sleep, fatigue, loss of appetite, changed bowel movements—are found, and the rate of adjustment of the body rhythms to a simulated time-zone transition is similar to that observed after real transitions.

Thus, many of the problems of time-zone transitions can be modelled in the laboratory where travel difficulties are no longer relevant. Even so, becoming angry when travel arrangements go wrong can hardly help. In brief, *keep calm*. The laboratory experiments also exclude the time spent on the actual flight itself. As we shall see, this can be an important part of the battle against jet-lag.

It is due to a change of life-style

The 'change of life-style' argument is unsound because the change is not necessarily greater the further you fly or the more time zones you cross. Consider, for example, the cultural differences for a European in journeying to parts of Africa (large, but few time zones crossed) or New Zealand (smaller cultural changes but more time zones crossed). The traveller to New Zealand from England has more jet-lag to contend with than the traveller to Africa.

In addition, jet-lag is experienced on returning home after a stay in another country, when the traveller is returning to his own culture. Alterations in diet and even hygiene might well produce indigestion and 'traveller's tummy', but this does not exclude the possibility that the time-zone transition produces similar or additional changes. Simulated time-zone transitions in the laboratory, where the diet remains unchanged, confirm that the change in local time produces a change in appetite and bowel movements.

It is a matter of experience

It could be argued that, with practice, the body becomes more able to adjust to a time-zone transition, a kind of 'learning' effect. Some travellers maintain that they get used to jet-lag but others find that the problem becomes worse. Travellers might get used to jet-lag in the sense that they learn to live with it, or they might find it progressively more irksome as their initial excitement with travel begins to wear thin. The idea that the body clock might adjust more readily with practice is an attractive one, but there is no evidence to support it. What might arise with practice is a better routine for coping with jet-lag, and this is the aim of the next chapter.

Adjusting the body clock

Accepting that the body clock is slow to adjust to a time-zone transition, our aim must be to speed up this adjustment. Adjustment will be speeded up if we can strengthen the time-cues in the new time zone. To recapitulate what we described in Chapter 2, the main examples are our rhythms of:

● Sleep and naps;

● Physical activity (including exercise, walking, gardening);

● Business activity (including appointments, shopping, office hours);

● Social influences and leisure time (including the pub, disco, theatre, parties);

● Mealtimes;

● Exposure to natural daylight and darkness.

Under normal circumstances these different rhythms give the same information about external time; that is, they reinforce one another. This can be seen when the differences between night (when it is dark, quiet and we sleep) and day (when we arrange our meals, our business, social and physical activities and it is a noisier, more 'active' environment) are considered. In practice, during our waking hours we are subject to social conventions and personal routines which jointly determine when we eat, relax, work, have parties, etc. Those who, day by day, show regular habits and who are subjected to these external influences in a regular way possess body clocks that are more accurately adjusted to 24 hours than do those whose life-style is less regular (see Fig. 2.4 and pp. 97–99, for example).

Such knowledge will be the basis of the advice we give in the next chapter for promoting adjustment after a time-zone transition.

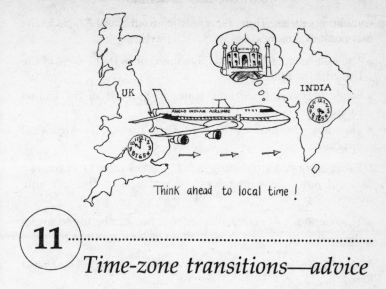

Think ahead to local time !

11

Time-zone transitions—advice

Advice on time-zone transitions depends very much upon the kind of journey being made, so we consider the following possibilities:

- A flight crossing only a few (one or two) time zones;
- A flight crossing several time zones, (to the west or east) and when the stop-over, before returning home, is short;
- A flight crossing several time zones to the west where there is sufficient time and need for adjustment to the new time zone;
- A flight as in the last example, but to the east.

How far is your journey?

Table 11.1 gives a general guide to the number of time zones between the United Kingdom and other countries. Corrections might have to be made if Single or Double Summertime (Daylight Saving Time) is in operation. If the journey does not start or end in the United Kingdom then the list can be used by combining entries. Thus, for a journey from Saudi Arabia to the east coast of America:

- The east coast of America is five time zones to the west of the United Kingdom.
- Saudi Arabia is three time zones to the east of the United Kingdom.
- Therefore the journey is eight time zones in a westward direction.

If the country you are visiting is not listed in Table 11.1, you can find out how many time zones distant it is by the following means:

- The telephone directory. The information can be found under the section on international dialling codes.

Table 11.1 Time-zones in hours to the west (W) or east (E) of the United Kingdom

	Time-zone difference	Local time when noon GMT
New Zealand	12	midnight
Australia	8–10 E	2000–2200
Japan	9 E	2100
China	8 E	2000
Singapore	8 E	2000
Delhi	5½ E	1700
East Africa	3 E	1500
Saudi Arabia	3 E	1500
Moscow	3 E	1500
Central and South Africa	2 E	1400
Eastern Europe	1 E	1300
West Africa	No time difference	noon
Greenland	3 W	0900
Brazil	2–4 W	0800–1000
East coast of Canada	3 W	0900
East coast of USA	5 W	0700
West coast of South America	5 W	0700
Midwestern States of USA /Canada	6–7 W	0500–0600
West coast of USA/Canada	8–9 W	0300–0400
Alaska	11 W	0100

● A world atlas. Some give the time zones directly. If not, they can be estimated by knowing that one time zone equals 15° longitude. Thus Christmas Island (105°E) is seven time zones to the east and Jamaica (75°W) is five time zones to the west.

But be warned, not all countries abide exactly by these rules, and so slight regional modifications are quite common.

Since all journeys start with a flight, we will first advise briefly on suitable behaviour during the flight.

What to do during the flight

The anxieties associated with a journey and the change of routine can cause a general sense of fatigue which will often be increased by loss of sleep as a result of the timing of the journey. Another problem arises because the air on board the aircraft has an oxygen pressure and water vapour content that are low in comparison with 'fresh air' and such an environment tends to cause dehydration and headaches. Further, the lack of movement that is possible during the flight can lead to stiffness, even cramp.

Drinks

Coffee, tea, and alcohol are likely to be offered, but try to limit how much of these you drink. This is not a 'killjoy' attitude but an attempt to guard against the dehydration produced by the dry air in the cabin. All these drinks possess diuretic properties, that is, they increase the loss of body fluids in the urine. Fruit juices, squashes and spa waters are recommended alternatives. Still drinks are better than fizzy ones (because of the reduced air pressure that exists in an aircraft cabin during a flight.)

Food

Foods necessarily tend to be of the 'convenience' type and low in fibre ('roughage'), and so might cause constipation later on. Try instead to eat foods that are higher on roughage; fresh fruit, wholemeal bread or rolls, celery, or carrots are all important sources of roughage. You might even take some fresh fruit with you for the journey.

Exercise

Try to get some exercise during the flight to decrease stiffness and the possibilities of cramp and swollen ankles. For some, a stroll down the aisles is sufficient, but isometric exercises (alternate tensing and relaxation of muscles) or those involving only limited movement (of the neck, back, arms and legs, for instance) can be performed conveniently within the confines of your seat. One enterprising airway promotes this idea by showing an in-flight video that leads passengers through such a work-out.

Sleep or naps and waking time

Boredom and fatigue will lead to the tendency to take naps but whether this should be encouraged or resisted depends upon details of the journey. This is discussed below. With some airlines, there is the facility (for example the 'sleeperette', to take a good sleep rather than just a nap).

A flight crossing only a few time zones

If you are flying to the east and crossing only one or two time zones or flying to the west and crossing three or less time zones, you are unlikely to suffer from the effects of jet-lag. Even so, you are advised to leave at least one clear day between the flight and an important business meeting. During this spare time you can catch up on lost sleep (as long as your naps do not prevent a full night's sleep), relax after the stresses of the journey, adjust drinking and eating habits, and generally adapt to your new surroundings.

During the flight you are advised to sleep or nap if it is night time. If it is daytime try reading a book, talking, playing cards, etc. *but do not nap.*

A flight crossing several time zones but only a short visit

If your stay in the new time zone is brief (1 or 2 days), then a substantial adjustment to it is unlikely. Therefore you are advised to arrange important meetings at times coincident with daytime on your home time and to avoid times coincident with night on home time. After a flight to the east, meetings should take place in the latter half of the daytime rather than in the morning by new local time. After a flight to the west, meetings should take place in the morning by new local time rather than in the latter part of the day. If you feel tired, a short sleep before an important meeting can be beneficial as long as it ends at least one hour before your meeting to make sure that you have woken up fully. Sleeping pills are not advised unless they are short-acting benzodiazepines whose effects wear off in time (see p. 124).

A flight crossing several time zones and staying at your destination for several days

If your stay is longer, then you can attempt to promote adjustment of your body to the new time zone. This entails matching your life-style to that of the new time zone as fully and rapidly as convenient. This will have the effect of strengthening the time-cues which cause adjustment of the body clock. We stress that this advice will not remove jet-lag but should minimize its duration. In many cases, following the advice, particularly with regard to sleep, will initially be against the 'natural' dictates of the body clock, but, as we have explained, obeying the body clock in this case will only prolong the difficulties in living with the new time zone.

Example one—a flight to the west

This requires you to delay your body clock, which tends to be comparatively easy since it naturally tends to run rather slowly.

Before the flight

Can you begin to adjust your life-style to the new time zone in the days immediately before departure? One possibility is to go to bed one to two hours later than normal each night and get up one to two hours later each morning. Of course this might not always be possible. It is rarely useful to try and adjust fully to the time-zone transition before the journey, since this will interrupt your life-style too much.

During the flight

Set your watch immediately to agree with local time at your destination. During the flight try to sleep if it is night time at your destination and, when it is daytime there, try to stay awake—find somebody to talk to, a book to read or watch the in-flight movie. If required, the facility to take a good sleep can be a great advantage over having to try to nap in your seat. Be warned, however, that there are two practical problems that might arise if you attempt to adjust your habits in the ways suggested. First, the in-flight schedule is sometimes arranged in accord with time in your departure zone. Second, if you have to break your journey or change flights, make sure you use the appropriate local time for making the connection.

After the flight

ADOPT THE NEW LOCAL TIME FOR ALL ASPECTS OF YOUR LIFE-STYLE

Sleep

Since the new local time will be behind your body clock's time, you will tend to wake too early and feel ready for sleep in the afternoon or early evening. Recommendations are:

- Try to sleep in surroundings that are as quiet, dark, and comfortable as possible.
- If you wake early (often because you need to pass urine), stay quietly in bed until the correct rising time after having emptied your bladder.
- If you feel tired during the day, *resist* the temptation to take a nap. For the first day or so after the flight you might find it

helps to retire to bed one or two hours earlier than your normal time—but no earlier than that!

Physical activity and natural light

Light exercise and brisk walks taken at your accustomed time by the new local time will help to adjust you to the new time zone and to make you feel ready for sleep at bedtime. A particularly good time to be out-of-doors in natural lighting in the first two to three days after the flight is that corresponding to the evening and first part of the night on 'old time', 9 o'clock to 3 o'clock; this should help to delay your body clock. By the same token try to avoid bright natural light for the first two to three days after the flight at times corresponding to 5 to 11 o'clock in the morning on old time as this will tend to advance your body clock. Table 11.2 gives examples of this advice in practice.

Social activities

Provided that they do not stop you going to bed at the proper time, social activities are a very good way of adjusting to the new time zone, particularly if they enable you to spend time out-of-doors in natural daylight at the times recommended in Table 11.2.

Table 11.2 Good and bad times for exposure to natural light in the first two to three days after a time-zone transition

	Bad local times for exposure to natural light	Good local times for exposure to natural light
Time zones to the west		
4 hours	0100–0700*	1700–2300†
8 hours	2100–0300*	1300–1900†
12 hours	1700–2300*	0900–1500†
Time zones to the east		
4 hours	0100–0700†	0900–1500*
8 hours	0500–1100†	1300–1900*
12 hours	Treat this as 12 hours to the west	

* This will tend to advance your body clock
† This will tend to delay your body clock

Meals and drinks

- Try to make meals of the 'correct' type (breakfast, lunch, etc.) at your adjusted times. Do not take a large supper which may make sleep difficult immediately afterwards.

- There is some evidence that high-protein foods (fish, meat, etc.) and caffeine-containing drinks (coffee, tea) are best taken in the morning and that a light snack rich in carbohydrates (fruit juice and dessert) is best for supper; caffeine-containing drinks should be avoided just before sleep.

- Alcohol is a *bad* 'nightcap'—it sends you to sleep, but will act as a diuretic and cause you to awaken to pass urine.

Example two—a flight to the east

After a flight to the east, your body is behind the new local time and to adjust to it you will have to advance your body clock. Because the body clock tends to 'run slow', advancing it is more difficult and this explains why it takes longer to adapt (see Table 11.3). Even so, the advice is similar in principle to that given for a westward flight.

Before the flight

If possible, try to adjust at least partially to the local time of your destination by going to bed one or two hours earlier each night and getting up one or two hours earlier each day.

Again this might not always be possible, but going to bed and getting up earlier are not likely to intrude too much upon your normal working life.

During the flight

The advice is the same as that given for westward flights— though, of course, whether people living in the new time zone are awake or sleeping will differ. Again, in-flight arrangements are sometimes timed with respect to the departure zone.

After the flight

ADOPT THE NEW LOCAL TIME FOR ALL ASPECTS OF YOUR LIFE-STYLE

Sleep

Since the new local time will be ahead of your body clock's time, you will tend to have difficulty in waking up and feeling alert during the morning. You will also tend not to feel tired by the time the local inhabitants are going to bed.

The advice is the same except that now the 'dangers' are:

● If you cannot get to sleep at night, stay in bed and rest. If this continues to be unsuccessful then some travellers purposely 'miss' the first sleep in their new time zone to make sure that they are tired on the second night.

● If you feel tired when it is time to get up—indeed, you might just be getting off to sleep!—do not stay in bed, but get up. A 'lie-in' of one to two hours *but no more* is permissible for the first day or so.

Physical and social activities, meals, and drinks

All the advice given for westward flights applies equally after flights to the east. Table 11.2 shows times when natural light is recommended or advised against. Now you wish to advance your clock so natural lighting at what was 5 to 11 o'clock in the morning on old time is good, but bright light at what was 9 o'clock in the evening to 3 o'clock in the morning is undesirable.

How long might jet-lag last?

Table 11.3 gives a guide to the duration of jet-lag that might be expected after a single journey. Older people tend to be nearer

Table 11.3 Estimates of how long jet-lag will last

Westward flights		Eastward flights	
Time zones crossed	Days to adjust	Time zones crossed	Days to adjust
0–3	0*	0–2	0*
4–6	1–3	3–5	1–5
7–9	2–5	6–8	3–7
10–12	2–6	9–11	4–9

* Day of rest recommended to recover from journey

Note: It is better to consider an eastward flight crossing 12 time zones as equal to a westward one crossing 12 time zones.

124   *Your body clock in disorder*

the upper limit of any range than do younger people, but some combination of the factors mentioned can help individuals approach the lower limits.

Drugs and jet-lag

For those on regular medication

Clearly, if you are required to take medications, the instructions 'first thing in the morning' or 'with meals' will involve some irregularity after a time-zone transition and change of routine have taken place. Unfortunately, it might not be just a matter of rescheduling 'waking time' and 'mealtimes' along the lines we have suggested above, since the body does not adjust immediately to the new routine. Consult your doctor if at all in doubt.

Drugs and other aids for overcoming the difficulties of jet-lag

Several possibilities come into this category and some have been mentioned earlier. Here we will summarize the position briefly. First there are the hypnotics which help you sleep and the stimulants which wake you up. We would always advise caution in the use of these because they might have side-effects and we suggest any unnecessary use of drugs is undesirable. Nevertheless, if a good sleep is imperative, say before an important meeting, then a short-acting hypnotic might be helpful (it needs to be short-acting or its effects might last into the next waking period). An alternative is to take a short nap before the meeting, making sure there is at least one hour between the nap and meeting so that you can waken fully. Alcohol is a poor way of getting a long sleep as its diuretic effect wakes you because of a full bladder. Stimulants in the form of pills are unnecessary; coffee, fresh air, and light exercise are effective substitutes.

There is no pill of which we are aware that can be relied upon to promote adjustment of the internal clock. Pills can now be bought which, it is claimed, can help this process but their worth has not been fully established scientifically. Moreover, some appear to consist of little more than the 'active constituents' of the dietary regimen we have already described—a regimen whose effectiveness is not accepted by all research workers.

Recent work has shown promising results for tablets containing melatonin. They can be taken a few hours before sleep is required in the new time zone. The results of scientific tests validate these tablets as a means of reducing the fatigue associated with jet-lag. It is not yet known if other symptoms of jet-lag are reduced and there is little clear evidence that they adjust the body clock that controls body temperature and performance rhythms. That is, they might act as does aspirin in the case of a headache in curing a symptom but without affecting the cause. Unfortunately melatonin is not yet commercially available.

Recently, an electronic device has been marketed which gives advice on when you should expose yourself to daylight at your destination. In this respect it is very similar to Table 11.2, therefore, the major difference being its cost.

In short, therefore, the best advice for combating jet-lag is to adopt a new routine in accord with your new time zone, to strengthen all possible time-cues, and so to reset the body clock as quickly as possible.

Enjoy your flight and trip!

12

Shift-work—the problems

We are essentially daytime creatures—awake in the daytime and asleep at night—and this is the reason why most of us work in the daytime, at a '9-to-5' job. For about 20 per cent of the work-force, however, some work at night is involved. Such an 'abnormal' pursuit affects all branches of the work-force. Thus, it is found in broadcasting, the hospital service, the fire-fighting force, police and military personnel, computer operators, food distributors, long-distance lorry drivers, workers in the chemical, mining, refining and steel industries, catering staff, hoteliers, coastguards—the list is almost endless. Often night-work is done as part of a shift system by which all shifts—daytime and night-time—are worked in rotation. For others, the hours of work might be abnormal, but regularly so; thus bakers and croupiers at casinos will all routinely work during some part of the night. Permanent night-workers exist also, individuals who work only at night; common examples are night-watchmen and machine operators in the newspaper industry.

Problems for shift-workers

Generally, the difficulties associated with shift-work are concentrated on the night-shift. Accordingly, we will concentrate on the night-worker in what follows and refer to other shifts only if they also result in some particular difficulty.

The main problems are social, domestic and health difficulties and chronic fatigue or tiredness.

Social and domestic factors

The night-worker has to make the most of what can be unsatisfactory social circumstances. Obviously, he or she is as likely as anyone else to be married with a family, to be single, and to have friends and the need for a social life. Since family and community life are normally orientated in accord with the leisure and working hours of the majority, night-workers are often excluded from sharing family mealtimes and leisure activities or participating in sporting, cultural, or political associations. They might feel a sense of social isolation and resent being unable to attend a regular evening class or even to follow serialized television programmes. Sexual and marital problems are more frequent among shift-workers. There is less opportunity for sexual relations and less sharing of child-rearing responsibilities. Leisure time and rest days need to be used well, therefore, to maintain contacts with the family, friends and neighbours. There is a tendency, however, for friends to come from a circle who also work at night since inconveniences in common can draw people together.

There are, even so, some advantages to shift-work which should not be forgotten—access to shops and other services during less busy hours, the opportunity to follow sports such as golf and fishing, which day work seldom permits, and more frequent three-day breaks, allowing time to 'get away from it all'. It is probably these considerations that lead to some night-workers actually enjoying night-work. Even so, it is common practice for them to revert fully to a 'normal', day-orientated lifestyle during rest days. Importantly, part of the advice (Chapter

12) will be to consider the positive rather than the negative aspects of night-work where possible.

Health

There are two main areas of complaint.

The first centres on gastro-intestinal disorders, the symptoms of which are problems with bowel movements, stomach aches, and loss of appetite. Gastric and duodenal ulcers are more frequently experienced by shift-workers than by their colleagues who work during the daytime only. These disorders are blamed on the irregular or 'abnormal' hours of work. There are, however, other factors that will contribute. The catering facilities at night are often absent or poor, with little choice beyond mainly fried or 'convenience' foods. As a result, some night-workers 'nibble' snacks rather than have a proper meal. In addition, many consume large quantities of coffee and cigarettes in a bid to stave off drowsiness, and others use alcohol to promote sleep. All of these factors (rather than just the timing of meals) may well induce gastro-intestinal disorders or exacerbate them.

The second area of complaint centres on sleep loss, with the resulting fatigue being blamed for feelings of malaise, for metabolic disturbances and even for mild forms of anxiety and depression. As yet, there is no evidence to implicate sleep deprivation as a major cause of serious illness. Even so, chronic fatigue can be debilitating and ways to reduce this are an important part of a night-worker's 'armoury'.

With regard to absence due to sickness, many researchers report *lower* rates in shift-workers. Workers who suffer most from the undesirable side-effects of night-work are those who have left it. In fact, it appears that those who have difficulties in adjusting are more likely to opt out of the system altogether than to endure long spells of sickness or absence. The finding of a low incidence of disorders in those that remain, therefore, might be misleading in that it might represent the fact that we are dealing with a self-selected group of workers. This finding also implies that workers differ in their ability to deal with night-work and this is a problem that we will consider later.

Chronic fatigue and further domestic problems

A common complaint amongst night-workers is their difficulty in obtaining sufficient sleep during the daytime. On average, they get at least one hour less sleep per day than when sleeping at night. Such a loss of sleep is not unexpected since the time when the night-worker has the opportunity to sleep tends to clash with his or her social and domestic responsibilities. Normal domestic routines will tend to be disruptive (housework is often noisy) and disrupted because children and spouses find it inconvenient always to have to remain as quiet as possible. In short, family accord is strained. The problem is worse, however, in that external factors—traffic, incoming telephone calls, neighbours and their children, etc.—also hinder sleep and often these cannot be controlled.

This loss of sleep is made up to some extent during rest days and, when the worker is on daytime shifts, by the more frequent use of naps. It has been shown that naps can make individuals feel refreshed and perform better. It is not known if they can fully make up for lost sleep, particularly in the long-term.

The morning shift, starting at about 6 o'clock in the morning, can be almost as great a cause of sleep loss as the night-shift. This arises because workers tend to maintain some social life in the evenings, and so go to bed too late to enable them to get a full night's sleep before having to rise at between four and five o'clock the next morning.

Many of these difficulties arise because of a clash between external factors but there still lurks an internal factor, one that relates to the basic biological fact that we are day-living, not nocturnal creatures. This internal factor is our daily rhythms and the body clock.

Night-work and the body clock

During night-work, our body clock will be telling us that we should sleep. We will feel tired, find work difficult and irksome and have difficulty in concentrating (see Chapter 5). If there is a large physical component in the work, that will appear more

tiring than usual (Chapter 4) and if there is one that requires
manual dexterity then, compared with the daytime, we will be
'all fingers and thumbs' (Chapter 5). Our appetite and digestive
system will be sending conflicting information (Chapter 6). On
the one hand, we will not have eaten for some time even
though we have been awake; on the other hand, our appetite
will be poor and we will not want a full meal. During the
daytime, even if our bedroom can be comfortable and quiet and
the family accepts that we need to sleep, we find we cannot sleep
(Chapter 3) or that it is fitful and that we have to get up to relieve
our bladder or empty our bowels (Chapter 6). All these daytime
problems arise because the body clock is now trying to wake us
up for a new day. In other words, when we start night-work our
body clock continues to remain adjusted to 'normal' habits—
daytime wakefulness and activity, and night-time sleep.

The change to night-work requires a marked change in the
timing of one's routine. It is found, however, that, whereas
adjustment to time-zone transitions is substantial after a few
days (see Chapter 11), for night-work it is slower. Adjustment is
slower because there is a *clash* between different time-cues. Thus
the individual might adjust his habits to fit in with the demands
of night-work, but he is aware that he is doing so in face of a day-
orientated society and is not exposed to daylight for much of his
period of wakefulness. Further, during his rest days, the
individual generally reverts to a 'normal' life-style (asleep at
nightime, awake in the daytime); now all time-cues constrain to
adjust him to this. Therefore, any hard-won adjustment to night-
work tends to be lost more quickly during days off or on day-
shifts. Again, in contrast to the result observed after a time-zone
transition, it has been found that rhythms appear to settle down,
and to adjust no further, after a few weeks on night-work, even
though their timing is still abnormal in some respects. For
example, on day work, many rhythms (including that of
temperature) tend to be in their rising phase (that is, temperature
is rising) during the work period, whereas they tend to be in
their falling phase during night-work. The explanation of this is
that in day-work the life-style after awakening is divided into the
sequence, work–leisure–sleep, whereas for the night-worker the
sequence is generally reversed, the worker sleeping in the

morning immediately after the night-shift. Thus, if a rhythm peaks at about the mid-point of the waking time, then it will be at the end of day-work but at the beginning of night-work. Note also that the night-worker is working during the second half of his activity so the effects of fatigue due to this cause (see Chapter 5) will be greater also. A worker could adopt the sequence work–leisure–sleep during night-work and this would aid fuller physiological adjustment, but it would also require sleep in the late afternoon and evening and this is a severe disadvantage socially.

Differences between the problems for the night-worker and the traveller across time zones

Even though the traveller suffering from jet-lag and the night-worker share some symptoms and the causes for them, the plight of the night-worker is far worse than that of the traveller. First, the changes can continue throughout the individual's working life. Thus, every time the shift changes, another change of routine and a temporary mis-matching between routine and the body clock will occur. Second, for all night-workers, even those who are permanent night-workers, there will be social pressures to adjust to a 'normal' existence during days of rest. These social pressures will be an influence even during work periods. Thus, unless the individual is a social 'loner' or part of an isolated community where shift-work is the norm, he will always be subjected to competing time-cues with regard to the timing his body clock should adopt. Moreover, his continual changes of work pattern will mean that his body clock can never settle down. An analogy would be a jet-setter forever crossing from one time zone to another and moving on before he had adjusted to his present time zone. It is not surprising that some workers leave night-work!

Differences between individuals where shift-work is concerned

In spite of all the possible difficulties, most workers do not leave night-work. For some, the problems of shift-work are minimal and offset by associated advantages and, for others, the advantages (spare time, money, promotion) act as powerful incentives to spend years on shift-work. Even so, about 10 per cent of workers do not tolerate night-work and choose to work in the daytime only. (Members of this group are sometimes called 'drop-outs').

It is particularly with this last group in mind that we will consider whether there is evidence that predicts those who might find shift-work particularly troublesome. Regarding differences between workers, these range from factors we can do little about (but should, even so, be aware of) to those that are far more under our control. These latter can be the basis of advice to individuals when it comes to dealing with shift-work.

Age

Shift-workers who cope happily for many years may, from their late forties onwards, start to experience difficulties. Although as a rule the total sleep requirement of older people decreases, they frequently experience an increased desire to take short 'naps'. Drowsiness on shift-work can therefore constitute a problem.

People over fifty years of age are generally less flexible physiologically and psychologically, and the capacity to adapt may be reduced in those who are unfamiliar with shift-work.

Flexibility of sleeping and waking habits

People differ also in their abilities to 'nap' when opportunities arise, to overcome feelings of drowsiness and in the ease with which they can turn over and go back to sleep (rather than get up and complain) when woken during daytime sleep. These differences not only reflect the psychological make-up of an individual but also indicate his or her commitment or motivation (see Chapter 13).

The timing of daily rhythms

'Larks' or 'morning types'—those with daily rhythms that rise earlier in the morning and fall earlier in the evening (Chapter 1)—are better able to go to sleep and get up early and so are more suited to the morning shift. By contrast 'owls' or 'evening types'—with slightly delayed rhythms when compared with most of us—are better suited to night-work, since they can 'lie-in' till the afternoon and so get more sleep after having gone to bed at about 7 o'clock in the morning.

Obviously neither group is generally advantaged with rotating shift systems in which all shifts are worked in sequence.

13

Shift-work—advice

We have considered and explained where possible the problems that are associated with night-work. We have also considered the factors which appear to affect the ease with which individuals can adjust to it. On the basis of this we can offer advice with respect to the least troublesome types of shift schedule involving night-work, and the means by which a worker can deal best with his particular schedule.

Are there workers who should be warned against night-work?

There are certain groups who would be advised to think very carefully before performing night-work and to seek careful medical counselling. These groups include the following:

Epileptics

Epileptics are more susceptible to seizures when fatigued and so cumulative sleep loss should be avoided. The morning shift from 6 o'clock in the morning to 2 o'clock in the afternoon is also likely to be associated with sleep loss, particularly for those who are 'owls', since they will have difficulty in getting to sleep early enough in the evening.

Asthmatics and those with respiratory disorders

Allergic reactions (to house dust, etc.) are often worse overnight, due in part to low concentrations in the blood of the hormone cortisol during the early hours (see Fig. 3.2). This is one reason why asthma symptoms are more marked at night, and substances at work such as dust, lint and chemicals might worsen the position.

Diabetics and others taking medicine regulary

A problem for all who regularly take drugs is the interpretation of instructions such as 'three times per day with meals', or 'once a day on rising', if their schedules are continually being changed. For example, the diabetic's insulin regimen will be very difficult to judge accurately with irregular mealtimes and for this reason he would be advised against shift-work in general. As a further example, arthritic pain is often worst in the morning—due in part to a lack of cortisol—and some medication is often taken at night, when cortisol concentrations are low, to reduce pain on waking. With a changed sleep/wake schedule, should the patient be advised to take the medication always before bedtime or to try and take it instead at a time coincident with the lowest concentration of his plasma cortisol? If the latter advice is given, by how much will his cortisol rhythm have adjusted to the changed schedule?

We reiterate that individuals are advised to seek medical advice if any of the above issues cause them concern.

Advice on the organization of shift systems

There are many types of shift system. In general, they differ in the number of hours worked each shift, the direction of rotation of shifts and the speed of rotation of shifts.

How long should the shift last?

Conventionally, shifts last 8 hours but there has been a trend recently towards 12-hour shifts, normally divided between 'night' and 'day' shifts. The 12-hour night-shift raises the question: what are the effects of extended work hours? The following general comments summarize the position that was described in more detail in Chapter 5.

- For 'interesting' and varied tasks, performance will be less likely to fall off appreciably with an extension of work time from 8 to 12 hours.

- For repetitive, boring tasks requiring vigilance or physical effort, performance might deteriorate, or at least be harder to sustain during these extra hours.

- As with shifts of any length, performance, especially in boring tasks and those requiring vigilance, tends to worsen if an individual is suffering from sleep loss and when daily rhythms are at their lowest point.

The implications of this are that, particularly with 12-hour shifts, attempts to change the type of task being done during the course of the shift should be rewarding to staff and management alike.

When should the shifts start?

A common arrangement for a three-shift system is for shifts to start at 6 o'clock in the morning, 2 o'clock in the afternoon and 10 o'clock in the evening. The difficulty here is the earliness of the start of the morning shift which means that workers will often have to get up at between 4 and 5 o'clock in order to reach work by this time. This is very acceptable for 'larks'—since they will be able to get to sleep early enough the previous evening— but it is rather early for most of us and, as has been mentioned already, fatigue is associated with the morning shift as much as with work at night. Starting the morning shift at 7 o'clock alleviates this problem, but some workers dislike the loss of afternoon spare time that the later start entails. The other shifts will have to start at 3 o'clock in the afternoon and 11 o'clock at night, of course, and there is also the difficulty that the afternoon shift ends later (at 11 o'clock) and this reduces the opportunity to chat with friends over a drink after work. Some see this as a major disadvantage. A more 'adventurous' scheme would involve an arrangement whereby individuals could choose to work one set of shifts (starting at 6 o'clock in the morning, 2 o'clock in the afternoon, etc) or the other (7 o'clock in the morning, 3 o'clock in the afternoon, etc) depending upon personal preference. With a little co-operation between all concerned, continuous working could be maintained.

In which direction should shifts rotate and when should rest days be taken?

If shifts are rotated, then the direction of rotation should be delayed rather than advanced. That is, the sequence of shifts 'morning–evening–night' is preferable to that of 'morning–night–evening'. The reason is that the body clock, with an inherent period greater than 24 hours, will adjust better to delaying rather than advancing shifts. There is also the general advice that days off should be taken after night-work, so that any accumulated sleep loss due to poor daytime sleep can be made up. It is sometimes argued that the counter-clockwise rotation (morning–night–evening) is better as it gives a longer break between the end of the night-shifts (say Friday night) and the next period of work (Monday evening rather than morning). Since individuals generally feel more tired with this system they tend to spend this extra free time 'recovering' in bed!

How rapidly should the shifts rotate?

We do not know whether a rapid (every day or so) or a slow (weekly or slower) rotation of shifts is to be preferred in the long term. No data are available to enable us to compare health

problems in individuals who are equal except for the speed of
rotation of the shifts that they work.

When the speed of rotation is considered, the problems of
cumulative sleep loss and social disruption are potentially most
marked when a slow rotation of shifts is involved. A worker in
this case will benefit greatly from colleagues, friends and a
family who understand and accept the difficulties. On the other
hand, a slow rotation of shifts does give the greatest opportunity
for adjustment of life-style and the body clock to night-work.

Where a weekly rotation of shifts is practised, this does not
give enough time for rhythms to adjust much but it does raise
the issue of social acceptability. For many people, long stretches
of night-work are undesirable but weekly stretches are more
acceptable. Further, the unit of social planning is often the week,
with special importance being attached to the regular occurrence
of weekdays, days for shopping, etc. It is for these reasons that
many prefer a weekly rotation of shifts.

In greatest contrast to permanent night-work are the 'con-
tinental' or 'metropolitan' systems by which shifts rotate every
one or few days. In such circumstances, adjustment is not
possible and so, on every occasion that night-work is being
performed, body rhythms will be timed appropriately for sleep.
This is likely to reduce performance on the night-shift, especially
if tasks are repetitive or require prolonged concentration. With
this rate of rotation, however, cumulative sleep loss will be
minimized.

In general, the rate of shift rotation should be slow only if
there is a reasonable chance that daytime sleep can be taken
satisfactorily. If that is not so then a more rapid rate of rotation is
recommended.

Advice to the work-force

There are several areas where advice can be given to individuals.

How to combat fatigue during night-work

Where possible, try to rouse yourself by a breath of fresh air or a burst of exercise. Other methods have included deep breathing, sucking a slice of lemon and pinching oneself. Again, if this is possible, try to change the kind of task you are doing (can you exchange with a colleague?) so that things become less boring. During breaks, particularly the 'lunch break' in the middle of the shift, try to chat to your friends or do something, rather than just 'hang about'.

Sleep and naps

We hope the need for as much sleep as possible—and this requires the co-operation of others living with you—has been stressed sufficiently. A quiet, darkened bedroom is best and with it the opportunity to escape from the telephone, etc. Earplugs and relaxation exercises might both be useful. Alcohol, as we have said, is a bad 'nightcap' before retiring as it will tend to cause your bladder to fill and so waken you.

Be prepared to make use of naps to 'top up' lost sleep. Often a nap after lunch (2 o'clock) is a good idea since most people feel tired then anyway, because of the 'post-lunch dip'. Naps later in the day are also useful before night-work.

Leisure time

Do not mope—get up and use your leisure time. You can arrange spare time (particularly if you take your leisure time before your sleep) when there are fewer crowds and there is less queuing for appointments or shopping than is the case for day workers. Make use of it also for hobbies, excursions, and leisure pursuits. Remember that Monday does not have to be 'wash day' and that Sunday is not the only day that leisure can be taken.

Meals

Do not skimp on meals. It is wrong for your digestive system to 'nibble' your way through night-work or to make do with endless cups of coffee or tea—often also with too many cigarettes. Structure your eating habits as much as you would on a normal daytime routine. 'Elevenses', 'tea-time', and a 'lunch break' should all be fitted into working hours and so become part of the normal night-shift routine. If possible, join your colleagues for these breaks, particularly 'lunch'. For lunch, try a fairly substantial meal. If you have a cafeteria then cut down on fry-ups and concentrate rather upon pasta or salads, for example. Even without a cafeteria, the advent of the microwave oven means that a more appetizing warm snack can be prepared with ease.

General advice

With a slow rotation of shifts you should make every attempt to adjust to night-work; this involves your eating and sleeping habits as well as your hours of work.

With a rapid rotation of shifts, the problem will be mainly one of combating fatigue on the night-shift as you will not be at all adjusted to it. To guard against the possibility of becoming disorientated you are advised to structure your life-style with a conventional, day-orientated routine as far as possible. This will involve your activity, sleep and mealtimes in particular. The usefulness of naps has already been mentioned; do not, however, take a nap too near to a time when you plan a full sleep. Thus, if you are on early shift and so will go to bed quite early, restrict naps to soon after lunch; naps in the evening will lessen your chances of a proper sleep later on.

If you have just come off late shifts then you will be used to late nights and lie-ins. If you are due to have a few days rest before night-work, then keep to late sleep times and lie-ins. This way you will be more ready for staying up all night.

The experienced night-worker

Shift-workers who have worked at night for a number of years and, therefore, who presumably tolerate it quite well, often structure their lives around the demands of night-work and place social life second. For others who find night-work difficult, social life often takes precedence over sleep and mealtimes. Not only the priority between work and social life but also the degree of structuring of activities can differ. Thus the worker tolerant of night-work often appears to arrange his day more than the worker who has difficulty with night-work. This might include regular times for shopping, housework, walking the dog, visiting the 'local', or taking meals. Without such a routine some workers can become disorientated. Such a structuring of the day might act as a set of 'personal time-cues', but in addition they might be reflections of the fact that the individual is unprepared to let the abnormality of routine required by night-work cause disruption of a full life-style.

Unfortunately, such intentions can be thwarted. (The problems of sleep-loss for those living in crowded housing have already been mentioned.) Also it is likely that mothers working on shifts and attempting to care for young children during the day will lose out on sleep; so both they and, ultimately, their families will suffer from the consequences. Furthermore a problem might exist with some workers whose socio-cultural habits conflict with some aspects of shift-work. For example, Moslems who are required at times to fast during the day may have to rely on the canteen facilities of the night-shift to provide their chief source of nutrition.

Perhaps many of the points we have raised can be assimilated into a model that describes a 'committed' or 'motivated' shift-worker. He or she will accept the changes in life-style that are involved and attempt to make use of the advantages it offers rather than be irked by the disadvantages. This will require a dedication to work and a careful and positive use of leisure time. This positive attitude will manifest itself as a regular life-style with regard to times of sleep, mealtimes, and times for chores such as shopping and appointments.

Conclusion and summary

Biologically, the position with regard to shift-work in general and night-work in particular is unsatisfactory. Clearly, factors such as financial reward and promotion can outweigh biological difficulties and the advice above might ameliorate many of them. Even so, for some workers, the disadvantages will outweigh the advantages and they will have to leave night-work.

If it is accepted that night-work must be done, then it must also be accepted that some will suffer and our role will be to recognise these individuals or even predict who they might be. There is the consolation that if an individual 'drops out' from night-work then any disturbances tend to disappear or, at the least, not to get worse. If he stays in night-work, any problem will almost certainly worsen.

To a large extent the ability to deal successfully with shift-work is up to the individual. Other factors—some biological, and others resulting from the attitude of colleagues, friends, or those in the work environment—will make things easier or harder, but ultimately it requires each individual to develop a positive attitude to shift-work, by stressing its advantages and by playing down or minimizing as many bad influences as possible.

Very recently, attempts have been made to promote adjustment to night-work by the use of pills containing melatonin or by bright artificial light. There is a close parallel here with work that has been done to combat jet-lag (see Chapter 11). It must be remembered that there are some circumstances (overnight driving, the use of video display units, for example) in which such methods are impracticable. Even so, preliminary results are encouraging and they are just one example of the continuing research into this complex problem.

14

Daily rhythms and medicine

Hospitals tend to be day-orientated in that administrative and consultative business, operations and treatment, cooking and maintenance of the building, all tend to take place during the daytime. This is to be expected, of course, and is for the convenience of both the staff and patients. Equally clearly, the hospital cannot shut at night; it must continue to look after the patients, to be able to deal with emergency admissions, and to provide medical care whenever required. Emergencies might occur at any time. Accidents occurring in the workplace will concentrate during the daytime, while those in the house, such as falling down stairs, might be more frequent early in the morning or late at night. Accidents due to sport will occur at the weekend, on Saturday afternoon in particular, and those resulting from brawls will be mainly on a Friday or Saturday evening.

Time of day, death and birth

Other emergencies or situations that require immediate attention can also be distributed unevenly around the clock.

Problems due to a heart attack, blood clot, or stroke all tend to be slightly concentrated in the hours from about 6 o'clock in the morning to noon. This result is thought to be produced by a combination of several circumstances that exist at these times of day:

- The tendency for the blood to clot is higher.

- Blood pressure is rising most rapidly from its night-time minimum to a maximum at about 11 o'clock in the morning (see Now Try This—7 at the end of this Chapter).

- The individual is undergoing the stress associated with the rigours of starting a new day.

As a result, the physical demands made upon the heart and blood vessels, when they have to deal with higher pressures and the challenges from an individual's environment and life-style, are greatest at the same time as the circulation is most susceptible to blood clotting.

To strike a happier note, the rate of child births is higher during the latter hours of the night than at any other time of the 24 hours. The reason for this is partly because the mother's labour tends to start in the late evening. There are at least two reasons why this should be so and they show, once again, that there are external and internal causes to a rhythm. The external cause is because the mother is more likely to be lying down in the evening than at other times of the 24 hours. This promotes kicking movements of her unborn child because the pressure inside the mother's abdomen, which acts upon the fetus, changes when she alters her posture, and because the fetus is responding to a modification of blood flow from the placenta. The body can influence the rhythm of labour onset due to hormonal rhythms in the mother and fetus. There are several hormones, all showing daily rhythms, that interact to modify the strength of contraction of the uterus muscle as well as its sensitivity to the fetus's movements. It is believed that this combination of factors leads to the population as a whole showing a daily rhythm in the onset of labour.

It will be noted that childbirth will tend to occur at night when hospital staff are likely to be decreased in numbers and tired due to the difficulties of night-work. In spite of this, it is reassuring to know that childbirth in the night does not appear to be associated with more problems—indeed there is a report that births at night are *less* prone to difficulties than those in the daytime; the 'natural' time is best, as it were. Not surprisingly, Caesarean sections and induced births nearly always take place in the daytime, which is no more than a reflection of the desire to plan work to correspond to the daytime habits of most hospital staff.

Daily rhythms and diagnosis

In diagnosing an illness, the doctor will measure something which is known to become abnormal in the disorder he is investigating. Having taken into account features such as the age, sex, and build of the patient, his or her recent life-history, and statistical variation, the doctor can then decide if the variable is abnormally large or small.

Consider the example of body weight. How would we decide if a male was 'obese'? We would need to know whether his body weight was within the 'normal' range for a male of that age and height. 'Normal' is defined statistically on the basis of measurements made upon many healthy males of different ages and heights. We would also have to take into account genetic or cultural effects; consider the (genetic) differences between Eskimos and Negroes with regard to build, or between inhabitants of different countries when it comes to their diet (often cultural) and the effect this has upon body weight. The life-history of our male would be important also: we would expect him to be heavy—due to muscular development—if he had been undergoing athletic training, for example. Even taking into account all these factors, there would still be a range of values associated with health, just as there are ranges in hair colour, height, sensitivity to pollen, etc. within given races and groups of people. These differences are quite normal. We have to choose in our example a weight below which the majority of the population is expected to fall. Those who are above this are defined as being obese. In the same way, eccentricity turns into madness if it is too marked, stubble grows into a beard, the number of red blood cells becomes low enough to merit the diagnosis of anaemia, or body temperature becomes raised enough so that we are said to have a fever. Often the choice of a boundary is rather arbitrary, but at least it gives rise to a standardized value that can become a basis for the diagnosis of obesity or whatever.

When daily rhythms are involved, other problems arise. Consider the case of trying to assess if the release into the blood of growth hormone (the hormone that is mainly responsible for our increase in height during infancy and adolescence) is at fault in an individual who is particularly short. As Fig. 3.2 shows, this hormone is normally released in bursts that are concentrated during sleep, particularly during the first hour or so. A sample of blood collected during the daytime is unlikely to be useful since a low concentration is *normally* found at this time. The correct time of sampling is in the early hours of sleep. Conversely, if a patient is suspected of releasing too much hormone then daytime sampling, when blood concentrations should be very small, is required. These comments apply only to young men and women (the data of Fig. 3.2 will have been obtained from subjects of this age) because, as Chapter 7 has shown, there are differences in the pattern of hormones release if the individual is a child, is reaching puberty, or is quite old. In these groups, therefore, the most appropriate sampling times might be different.

As a further example of the importance of the time of diagnosis, reference to the daily rhythm of the concentration of cortisol in the blood (see Fig. 3.2) will indicate that a suspected lack should be assessed in the morning on waking and an excess in the evening. In summary, if the daily rhythmic changes are marked then the time of diagnosis is most important. A particularly clear example of this would be the diagnosis of the presence of certain threadworm parasites in the blood of a patient. Some species are present in the blood stream in the daytime and 'hide' in the lungs at night. For other species, the reverse holds, the parasite being detectable in the blood only at night. Clearly, apppropriate sampling times are vital in such cases.

By contrast, for many substances the time of diagnosis is less important, because the range of daily changes is too small. For example, the daily rhythm in the number of circulating red blood cells is not an important consideration when diagnosing anaemia, since the decrease in their number in this condition is far greater than occurs as a result of the daily rhythm.

Measuring one's own rhythms

It has been argued that a regular measurement of daily rhythms by an individual will give a 'personalized' health rhythm and that, with this information, small changes from the norm can be picked up. The argument continues that such 'advance warning' can better enable countermeasures to be taken. Earlier treatment is likely to be advantageous, of course, but there is no clear evidence that altered daily rhythms reliably precede an illness. There should be no doubt also as to the huge amount of measurement that would be required from individuals taking part in such a scheme. Gift catalogues now include apparatus for measuring one's own heart rate and blood pressure quickly and conveniently. The reader is warned, however, that converting large amounts of data into reliable estimates of daily rhythms is no easy matter; even so, a high blood pressure throughout the day would be a matter for concern and would indicate the need to take medical advice.

Altered daily rhythms as a sign of disease

In some disorders, altered daily rhythms will contribute to some of the symptoms. A knowledge of this can act as an additional diagnostic aid and the disappearance of abnormalities can help in the assessment of treatment. For example:

● In some cases of heart failure and renal disorder, particularly where fluid accumulation (oedema) takes place, the rhythm of urine flow can become inverted. There is an increased flow at night and this might well distress the patient by waking him or even by causing bed-wetting.

● In health, our airways are widest about noon (and so breathing is easiest then) and thereafter they narrow gradually until they show the highest resistance to air-flow during the

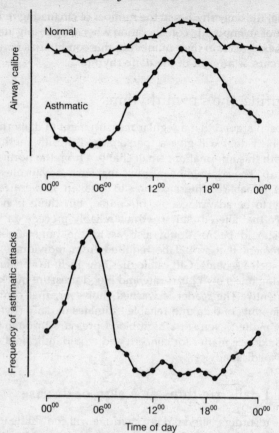

Fig. 14.1 Top: Relationship between time of day and airway calibre in normal subjects and asthmatic patients. Higher airway calibre shown upwards.
Bottom: Relationship betwen time of day and frequency of asthmatic attacks. Higher frequency shown upwards.

night. In some individuals this nocturnal increase is exaggerated so that, in extreme cases, a difficulty associated with breathing is particularly marked and asthmatic attacks, breathlessness, and general 'wheeziness' are most common then (Fig. 14.1). Asthmatic patients who are being treated for these attacks can get an estimate of whether their treatment is continuing to be successful by making simple measurement of airway resistance daily. (Some asthmatic attacks can be predicted because there is a deterioration in the individual for a few days beforehand.) Knowledge of the daily rhythm indicates that the best time to make such measurements would be in the evening or first thing on waking in the morning.

Daily rhythms and the patient's symptoms

In many cases, patients visit their doctors because of the development of symptoms of an illness, and these symptoms might show a daily rhythm in their severity. The example of an increased sense of breathlessness during the night has already been mentioned. Another common example is the severity of a fever as assessed by the first-line approach, namely, feeling the forehead. Assessed like this, fevers are generally more marked in the evening because this is when heat is being lost through the skin most quickly as the body is cooling down in preparation for sleep (see Chapter 2). A feverish brow is less common in the morning when the body is tending to minimize heat loss—and, for this reason, at that time it can be a clearer sign that something is wrong.

Allergic responses

Asthma is a form of allergy and it is now known that there is a daily rhythm in allergic responses in general. Thus injections (under the skin or up the nose) of various types of material causing allergic responses (pollen, house dust, etc.) cause a much more marked response (a wheal at the site of injection, itching and watering of the eyes and nose) in the evening than in the morning. The low blood concentrations of the hormone cortisol that are found in the evening (see Fig. 3.2) are implicated since this hormone is known to damp down these responses. There are external factors also, as anyone suffering from hay-fever will know! That is, even though an allergic response can be produced whenever the appropriate substance is present, in the evening it is either more marked or needs less irritant in comparison with the morning.

Rheumatoid arthritis

Rheumatoid arthritis is a disease of the joints in which there is inflammation, pain and stiffness, symptoms that arise because the immune system attacks the joints. The activities of the white blood cells, and therefore the severity of the symptoms that are experienced, are most marked in the morning (Fig. 14.2). They are normally controlled, once again, by the hormone cortisol. There is also an external cause of the daily rhythm of symptoms since stiffness is promoted by immobility of the limb. Thus, staying awake and active all night might reduce the stiffness and pain due to immobility but it does not entirely prevent the morning increase.

Pain

Pain is probably the symptom that is most widely used by us as a sign that all is not well. In general, the threshold for acute pain (for example, as after a pinprick) declines as the day progresses to reach a lowest value (that is, we are most likely to feel pain) in the late afternoon. In practice, thresholds and rhythms are unlikely to be a major consideration in such circumstances—we have hurt ourselves and minor differences in the amount of pain are irrelevant. With other types of pain (for example, an aching or dull pain from the gut) the daily rhythm often peaks during the night. Knowledge of the time of peak of such a rhythm, whenever it might occur, enables more pain-killing drugs to be given at the approriate time. Why different types of pain show different daily rhythms is often unknown though they all probably have internal and external causes. Internally, daily rhythms of naturally occurring, morphine-like substances, might play a role in determining how much pain we feel. When we lie still (see above), when we exercise a particular joint, and when we eat a meal and get indigestion are all common examples of ways in which rhythmicity in the external causes of pain can arise.

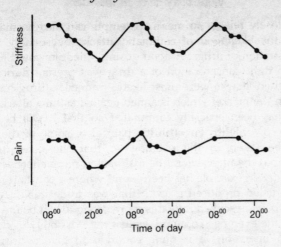

Fig. 14.2 Relationships between time of day and subjective ratings of stiffness and pain over three successive days in a patient with rheumatoid arthritis. Worse symptoms shown upwards.

Timing treatment

We have to got used to the idea of taking pills 'three times per day with meals', when rising in the morning, or just before retiring at night. In many cases this is useful mainly because it is a means of remembering when to take the pills. There are some circumstances, however, when other factors should be taken into consideration.

The drug is given when it is required most

Consider asthma, indigestion, or a headache. Obviously we take medication when we are suffering from symptoms of the disorder. For instance, we would inhale a substance producing widening of the airways if an asthma attack were threatened or taking place. If we are are particularly thoughtful (or pessimistic) we might even taken an indigestion pill *before* a meal, that is we predict when we might need a drug. Similarly, if diabetics are using a form of insulin that acts rapidly, they would take it at times closely related to meals. Attempts can also be made to reduce the likelihood of asthmatic attacks by suitably timed administration of drugs. A good dosing schedule would ensure that the right concentration of a drug was present during the night when attacks were most likely. (Indeed, a drug has just come on the market which is aimed against asthma attacks and which has been specially formulated so that it will be most effective overnight.) For arthritic pain also, some of the drug might be taken in the evening so that the concentration throughout the night would be maintained more effectively.

Recently an example has been found where a constant rate of drug infusion produced a result that was undesirable. As has already been described, blood is more prone to clot before noon than in the evening. To guard against the possibility of clotting after an operation, it is quite common to give a drug that prevents clotting, an anti-coagulant, by continuous intravenous drip. The same rate of infusion is generally used throughout the 24 hours. It was found that this rate of infusion could be too high in the evening (when the tendency to clot is naturally low) so that there was a risk of haemorrhage, and yet the same rate was too low in the morning (when the tendency of the blood to clot is higher) so that there was still a risk of clotting at that time.

Replacement therapy

Hormone replacement therapy provides further examples of treatments where the timing is important. The general rule would be to mimic the daily rhythm of the hormone in blood as closely as possible (see Fig. 3.2, for examples); thus, in the case of an artificial steroid (being administered as a replacement for cortisol), most would be given in the morning. The position is complicated, however, because hormones are released into the blood as a series of pulses, so making a jagged rather than a smooth 24-hour profile. It is now becoming apparent that dosage regimes which also take into account these complexities are most effective, as is shown by recent attempts to deal with problems associated with delayed onset of puberty and excessively short stature. Not only have the times of hormone injection mimicked what we know of the daily rhythm of the hormone in healthy individuals, but also the hormone has been given in a series of small bursts several times per day.

Chronopharmacology

The time when a drug should be given might be influenced also by the knowledge that its effectiveness can depend upon the time of administration. The study of this relationship between time and drugs is called chronopharmacology. There are two important applications of this. First, it might enable a drug to be given at a time when it has less unpleasant side-effects, as a result of which the drug can be given repeatedly for a longer period of time. Second, it might be possible to choose a time of administration when the amount of drug that needs to be given (and hence its cost) can be reduced.

These time-dependent effects of drug administration depend upon two interrelated factors:

- There are rhythmic changes in the sensitivity of the body to a fixed concentration of drug. This is a reflection of the daily rhythms in the number and properties of the sites on the cell surface which combine with the drug.

- When a drug is administered to a patient there is a rise followed by a fall in its concentration in the blood. This represents the time-course of the uptake of the drug, its distribution within the body, its breakdown by the liver, and its excretion by the kidneys. All of these factors show daily changes and so alter the time-course of the concentration of the drug in the blood and cells of the body.

As a result of these factors, there are rhythmic changes in the effectiveness of a drug upon the body as a whole. These rhythmic changes include not only the therapeutic effects but also the toxic side-effects of the drug. Clearly we wish to choose a time of administration of the drug which will maximize the ratio of therapeutic to toxic effects, that is, a time when the drug will do most good and least harm to the patient.

Cancer chemotherapy

These concepts of chronopharmacology can be illustrated by reference to cancer chemotherapy, a branch of therapeutics in which there are high hopes that an understanding of chronopharmacology will pay dividends. Cancer is a chronic illness and so prolonged drug treatment is necessary. The drugs are often very toxic and there is a small difference only between the dose required to produce a therapeutic effect (killing the cancerous tissue) and that which produces an unacceptably large toxic side-effect (killing or damaging the healthy issue).

The field is still in its infancy and is necessarily dominated by experiments upon animals. At the present time, clinical trials to establish if the same results are found in humans have only just begun. Interest has centred on the side effects of drugs that interfere with cell division; cancerous cells should be particularly sensitive to such drugs as they divide so rapidly. In addition, unlike healthy cells, they do *not* show a daily rhythm of cell division. Attempts to treat cancer, therefore, might involve giving the drug to the patient at a time when healthy cells are not dividing rapidly—due to the timing of their daily rhythm—but cancerous cells are.

Another approach is to administer the drug when its toxic effects upon the patient are smallest. A comparatively well-studied example is cisplatin, a drug that kills cancerous cells, but a side-effect of which is damage to the kidneys. Experiments in animals and humans have shown that this side-effect can be decreased by administering the drug with large volumes of fluid at a time when the kidneys are able to increase urine flow most (see Chapter 6). As a result, the drug is very dilute during its passage through the kidneys and more can be given without causing damage.

The development of mini-pumps

On several occasions—when considering the infusion of an anti-coagulant, hormonal replacement therapy and cancer chemotherapy, for example—we have mentioned the desirability of varying the rate of infusion of a drug or hormone during the course of the 24 hours. Normally this demands too much time from medical supervisors to be a feasible proposition. However, a device has been developed recently that might overcome the difficulties. It is a small pump that can be implanted into the body and releases drugs at the required rates throughout the day. The drugs are stored in a series of reservoirs and these can be replenished every month or so as required. The device is powered by a small battery and controlled by a microcomputer which controls the rate of release of the drugs from the reservoirs and can be programmed from outside the body. The apparatus will enable the doses of several drugs to be controlled, both during the course of a day and, day by day, as treatment progresses. Such a device is still in the experimental stage, but it is an exciting combination of miniaturization, computing, technology, and the application of a knowledge of daily rhythms.

Now try this—7.

A scientific problem—number 3

Drug X has been designed to reduce blood pressure in patients with high blood pressure. The graph (Fig. 14.3) shows a healthy subject's mean arterial blood pressure during the course of a normal 24-hour period; the mean arterial blood pressure of our patient living a normal life before treatment; and the mean arterial blood pressure of this patient during the 24 hours following treatment with drug X at 10 o'clock in the morning.

Does drug X control blood pressure? Our comments on this problem appear on page 157.

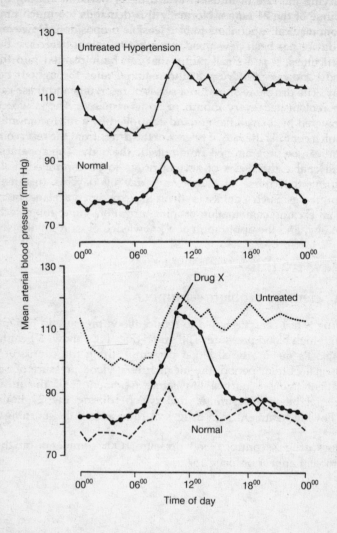

Fig. 14.3 Top: Mean arterial blood pressure in a healthy subject and in a patient with high blood pressure (hypertension).
Bottom: Hypothetical effects on blood pressure of administering drug X at 10 o'clock in the morning.

In many senses, X does control blood pressure. It lowers it to fairly normal values from about 2 o'clock in the afternoon (when the drug begins to take effect) to about 7 o'clock in the morning. Thus, it appears to be effective during the afternoon, evening, and most of the night. This would include times when our patient was awake and active as well as when he was asleep. By contrast, from 8 to 11 o'clock in the morning the blood pressure begins to rise above the values for a healthy individual and return to the 'normal' value for this patient. That is, drug X did not work after about 7 o'clock in the morning.

The effect of this is that there is a very marked rise in blood pressure between 8 and 10 o'clock in the morning and this coincides with the time when some fatal heart disorders are most common. This might be a cause for a considerable concern. Possibly the drug is no longer working by that stage (more than 21 hours after taking the drug) or it cannot reduce the morning rise. Either taking X at, say, 10 o'clock in the evening or taking half the dose at 10 o'clock in the morning and half at 10 o'clock in the evening are just two of the ways of deciding between such possibilities.

If the problem is that the drug only works for about 21 hours after taking the pill, then it is possible that this can be remedied quite easily (either as suggested above or by some form of the drug that is released into the blood stream more slowly). If the rapid rise between 8 and 10 o'clock in the morning could not be prevented by a single dose at 10 o'clock in the evening or by doses at 10 o'clock in the morning and evening, then severe doubts would be cast on the value of X.

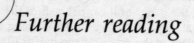

Further reading

1. Elementary
   G. G. Luce (1973) *Body Time*. Paladin, London.
2. More detailed account of daily rhythms in humans
   D. S. Minors and J. M. Waterhouse (1981) *Circadian rhythms and the human*. John Wright, Sevenoaks.
3. Broader, including annual and lunar rhythms, plants and animals
   D. S. Saunders (1977) *Biological rhythms*. Blackie, Glasgow.
   J. D. Palmer (1976) *An introduction to biological rhythms*. Academic Press, London.

Index

abnormal rhythms (*see also* rhythms) 95–107, 147–9

accidents (*see also* performance) 51, 53, 54, 143

activity (*see* bedtimes, mental activity, physical activity)

adjusting the body clock (*see* zeitgebers)

adrenalin (see hormones, physical activity)

ageing 33, 34, 73, 81–3, 101, 109, 123, 124, 132, 146

alertness (*see* fatigue)

allergy (*see* illness)

annual rhythms (*see also* rhythms) 3, 4, 98, 99, 103–7, 110, 115, 116

antidiuretic hormone (*see* hormones)

appetite (*see* mealtimes)

arthritis (*see* illness)

asthma (see illness—allergy)

athletes (see physical activity)

babies 30, 31, 68, 69, 73, 75–81, 86, 144–6
  premature 77, 80, 96

bedtimes (*see also* jet-lag, naps, sleep, night-work) 13, 18–20, 24–34, 36–8, 41, 42, 45, 48, 49, 75–8, 82, 83, 85, 87, 88, 97–102, 104, 107, 135

births 144, 145

blind people 28, 98, 99, 105

blood 20
  clotting 145, 152
  pressure 144, 155–7

body clock (*see also* jet-lag, night-work, shift-workers, zeitgebers) 9–13, 17–34, 40–2, 50, 51, 54, 63, 72, 73, 77–80, 82–91, 96–105, 107

adjusting (*see* zeitgebers)
  usefulness 88, 89, 110, 111
  where found 84–91

body temperature (*see also* thermal comfort) 6–8, 10–12, 19, 25, 35–38, 43, 45, 47, 48, 62, 64, 65, 76, 85–9, 98, 101, 102, 104, 110, 111, 125, 130, 131, 149

bowel movement (*see also* jet-lag, night-work) 70, 150–2

bright light (*see* daylight)

cancer (*see* illness)

cardiac disorders (*see* illness)

caves (*see also* isolation chambers, Poles) 20, 21, 23, 29

chronopharmacology (*see also* cancer) 73, 74, 153–5

circadian rhythms (*see* rhythms)

clock (*see* body clock)

comfort (*see* thermal comfort)

constant routines 10–12, 17, 78

cortisol (*see* hormones)

daily rhythms (*see also* rhythms) 3–5, 25, 26, 38, 76, 88, 89, 93, 126, 129, 145

daylight 29, 32, 85, 87, 96, 98, 103–7, 114, 121, 123, 130, 142

deaths (*see also* illness—cardiac disorders) 143, 144

deep sleep (*see also* sleep stages) 38, 40–2

depression 101–7

diabetes (*see* illness)

diagnosis (*see also* illness, symptoms, treatment) 73, 93, 107, 145–9

diet (*see also* jet-lag, shift-workers) 68, 69, 71, 72, 117, 118